FORREST I. BOLEY

Professor of Physics and Astronomy
Dartmouth College

PLASMAS— LABORATORY AND COSMIC

Published for
The Commission on College Physics

D. VAN NOSTRAND COMPANY, INC.

Princeton, New Jersey

Toronto   *London*   *New York*

D. VAN NOSTRAND COMPANY, INC.
120 Alexander St., Princeton, New Jersey
(*Principal Office*)
24 West 40 Street, New York 18, New York

D. VAN NOSTRAND COMPANY, LTD.
358, Kensington High Street, London, W.14, England

D. VAN NOSTRAND COMPANY (Canada), LTD.
25 Hollinger Road, Toronto 16, Canada

Published simultaneously in Canada by
D. VAN NOSTRAND COMPANY (Canada), LTD.

PRINTED IN THE UNITED STATES OF AMERICA

Preface

The purpose of this book is to discuss some of the fundamental characteristics of plasma and some of the varied situations in which the behavior of plasma is important. Both laboratory plasmas and naturally occurring plasmas are discussed, since much can be learned in each domain that is pertinent to the other. The organization and presentation of the material in this book is not a systematic development of the principles of plasma physics; books of this type already exist. Rather the intent is to provide a survey of some aspects of present-day plasma physics in a form suitable for nonspecialist reading. The inherently complex nature of certain interesting problems sometimes tends to make an elementary discussion of them a bit superficial, and failings of this type will be seen in this book. Nevertheless, this poor treatment of the reader is hopefully balanced by a reasonably rounded view of certain problems of current interest in this field of physics. In spite of the attempt to keep the mathematical aspects of the discussion minimized, it is readily observable that this minimum is by no means negligible. However, the mathematical content should be understandable to readers who have completed a first calculus course.

Thanks are due and herewith given to Dr. Edward U. Condon, former editor of the Momentum Series, for stirring the interest to write this book and to Dr. Klaus Halbach for valuable criticism.

FORREST I. BOLEY

Hanover, New Hampshire

Table of Contents

1   *General Properties*
      of a Plasma

A plasma is a collection of charged and neutral particles that satisfies certain criteria to be presented shortly. The electrons and ions constituting a plasma are produced by ionization of atoms or molecules. Only under special circumstances are plasmas formed in the natural environment at the earth's surface, where the requisite ionization energy is not commonly available. However, laboratory plasmas are readily produced. And, throughout almost all of the space away from the earth's surface, plasmas are indigenous.

Each of the particles comprising a plasma is acted upon by what at first sight is a bewildering array of forces. The charged particles possess Coulomb fields through which they interact with each other and with whatever electric and magnetic fields are externally applied. The neutral particles interact with each other via the short range forces that come into play only during close encounters. The charged particles interact with the neutrals via more complex polarization fields produced by distortion of the electron orbits during the close passage of the charged particles.

In an ordinary gas composed entirely of neutral particles it is convenient and usually necessary to characterize the effects of all these individual interactions in terms of some macroscopic variables that bear a close resemblance to observable quantities. In thermodynamic discussions, pressure, density, and temperature are common examples of such macroscopic variables that are, not surprisingly, also important for plasmas.

A link between the particle description and the macroscopic observable properties is provided by a statistical treatment of the particle motions. Because of the very large number of particles it is possible to develop this connection between their individual actions and the effects of those actions upon the gross behavior of the assemblage. That the numbers are adequate to allow a statistical treatment is seen from the fact that in a monatomic gas at 10^{-5} atmospheric pressure there are 2.69×10^{14} atoms/cm^3 at 15°C.

One of the most powerful influences upon plasma behavior is the electromagnetic interaction of the charged particles. Since the electrostatic fields of the charged particles drop off only as the reciprocal of the square of the distance, the electrostatic forces are long range and can act upon a considerable number of other particles. This interaction of substantial numbers of particles causes them to react in a collective manner to other forces. And this collective behavior constitutes the prime characteristic of a plasma. In § 1-1 the specific criteria that insure the collective behavior are discussed.

A description of the regions and circumstances in which plasmas occur is given in § 1-2 and later expanded in Chapters 3 and 4. In § 1-3 attention is given to the charged-particle motions as they are influenced by applied electric and magnetic fields. In § 1-4 the interactions of the various plasma particles among themselves are discussed. The last section of this chapter describes a few effects of the energy variability of the plasma particles.

§ **1-1　Conditions for Plasma Existence.**　In order to produce a plasma it is necessary to free electrons that are normally bound into atoms. From Table 1-1 it is evident that ionization energies

TABLE 1-1　*Ionization energies of a few atoms and molecules.*

Gas	Ionization Energy (eV)
Hydrogen	13.6
Helium	24.6
Lithium	5.4
Neon	21.6
Cesium	3.9
Argon	15.7
Mercury	10.4
Hydrogen molecule	15.4
Nitrogen molecule	15.8

for many elements run from several electron volts (eV) to a few tens of eV. (One eV is the energy acquired by an electron in falling through an electrostatic potential of one volt and equals 1.6×10^{-12} ergs). There are various means whereby these energies may be added to the atomic system to produce ionization; the essential requirement is for an atomic electron to acquire sufficient energy to escape the force field of the atom. Ordinarily the energy comes from collision events of one sort or another. Section 1-4 deals with the specifics of such ionizing events.

On the addition of the ionization energy to a fraction of the atoms of a neutral gas, an *ionized gas* is formed. If sufficient total energy can be added, the gas may be completely ionized with no neutral particles remaining.

Even a partially ionized gas can be affected by externally applied electric and magnetic fields and can conduct electric currents. The ions and electrons serve as charge carriers in somewhat the same way as they do in an electrolyte. Most importantly, the Coulomb electrostatic fields of the charged particles in the ionized gas will produce the interesting consequences of the collective effects mentioned before.

The presence of collective effects constitutes the primary plasma criterion. A quantitative measure of this criterion may be obtained from a determination of the distance to which the electric field of an individual charged particle extends before it is effectively shielded by the oppositely charged particles in the neighborhood. Such a calculation was first performed by Debye for an electrolyte. Assuming a large number of neighboring particles so that the electric field can be taken as a continuous function of distance, the shielding distance deduced by Debye is

$$D = (kT/4\pi n e^2)^{1/2} \qquad (1\text{-}1)$$

where the Boltzmann constant is $k = 1.38 \times 10^{-16}$ ergs/degree Kelvin and T is the effective temperature in degrees Kelvin (°K) of the particles of charge e of which there are n per unit volume. Although the precise applicability of Eq. 1-1 to an ionized gas remains in some doubt, D does provide a measure of the distances over which the influence of an individual charged particle is dominant. Beyond D the electric field, and hence the influence, of the individual particle is nil, and collective effects dominate.

Thus one quantitative criterion for the existence of a plasma is that the linear dimension L of the system be large compared to D.

The assumption of a large number of particles in the neighborhood to provide the smooth decrease in the field required for the deduction of D is a further criterion for the existence of a plasma. To insure this requirement, the number of particles within a sphere of radius equal to the Debye length must be much greater than one. The two criteria may be summarized as

$$D \ll L \qquad (1\text{-}2)$$

and

$$(4\pi n/3)D^3 \gg 1. \qquad (1\text{-}3)$$

We can show that Eq. 1-1 gives a plausible form for the minimum distance to which a collection of charges must extend if collective effects are to dominate the thermal agitation of the collection. To do so we equate the electrostatic potential energy of the charges to their thermal kinetic energy. Consider a sphere of radius r filled with particles of charge q. The potential energy per particle is Vq where V is the electric potential. Since only radial particle motions affect the potential distribution, the particle kinetic energy is that appropriate to a single degree of freedom, $\frac{1}{2}kT$. Here again k is the Boltzmann constant and T is the electron temperature. Equating potential and kinetic energy,

$$Vq = (\text{Total charge}/r)q = 4\pi r^3 nq^2/3r = \tfrac{1}{2}kT. \qquad (1\text{-}4)$$

Solving for the radius of the sphere,

$$r = (3kT/8\pi nq^2)^{1/2} \qquad (1\text{-}5)$$

is the distance at which the electrostatic potential energy of the collection equals the thermal kinetic energy. This distance contains the same functional dependencies as the Debye shielding distance given in Eq. 1-1 and suggests the origin of those dependencies: For a smaller radius of the collection than is given by Eq. 1-3 the thermal energy exceeds the potential energy, and thermal motions will dominate the electrostatically induced collective ones.

It is interesting to see what enormous electric potentials are associated with small deviations from charge neutrality. Consider a sample of plasma with ion density n_i and electron density n_e contained in a sphere of one cm radius. The potential is

$$V = (\text{Total charge}/r) = \tfrac{4}{3}\pi r^2 (n_i - n_e)e. \tag{1-6}$$

If a plasma of electron density $n_e = 10^{14}$ per cm^3 were to deviate from neutrality sufficiently so that n_i exceeded n_e by only one percent, the potential would be $V \approx 2 \times 10^3$ stat volts $= 6 \times 10^5$ volts! Such potentials can only be maintained by very special conditions such as those occurring in electrical insulators. They cannot be maintained in a plasma. A plasma tends to maintain a condition of electrical neutrality. Since there is little constraint to the motion of charged particles in a plasma except where magnetic forces act, the particles move freely to neutralize regions of excess charge.

Quasi-neutrality is thus a third, but not independent, criterion for the existence of a plasma and can be written

$$n_i \approx n_e. \tag{1-7}$$

The preceding discussion pertains to the steady-state plasma. However, these steady-state conditions are not sufficient to insure that collective plasma motions can occur. One of the fastest and most important of the collective motions is the bulk oscillation of the plasma electrons with respect to the ions. The frequency of this oscillation, which is now to be calculated, provides a meaningful time scale against which those mechanisms tending to destroy such collective motions may be compared.

We expect that the plasma electrons can oscillate collectively about the much more massive ions; the ion-electron Coulomb attraction provides the necessary collective restoring force. Figure 1-1 represents a plasma the electrons and ions of which have been slightly but collectively displaced relative to each other a distance δ that is small compared to the plasma thickness L. The electric field E produced in the plasma interior by the displaced charges is

$$E = 4\pi s, \tag{1-8}$$

where $s = en\delta$ is the charge per unit area of surface perpendicular to s due to the charge density n. The force per unit area acting on the electron in the plasma interior is the charge per unit area times E and equals $(Lne)E = 4\pi n^2 e^2 L\delta$. The mass per unit area upon which this force acts is Lmn, where m is the electron mass. Thus the equa-

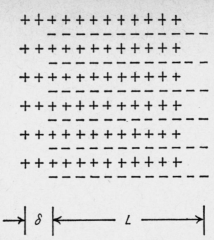

FIG. 1-1 A plasma sheet of thickness L with electrons and ions displaced a distance $\delta \ll L$.

tion of motion (mass times acceleration equals applied force) becomes

$$Lmn \frac{d^2\delta}{dt^2} = -4\pi n^2 e^2 L\delta, \qquad (1\text{-}9)$$

in which $d^2\delta/dt^2$ is the electron acceleration. Eq. 1-9 can be shown by direct differentiation to have the oscillatory solution

$$\delta = A \exp(i\,2\pi\nu_\mathrm{p} t), \qquad (1\text{-}10)$$

where

$$\nu_\mathrm{p} = (ne^2/\pi m)^{1/2} \qquad (1\text{-}11)$$

is the oscillation frequency, which is commonly called the *plasma frequency*. Expressed in cycles per second,

$$\nu_\mathrm{p} = 9 \times 10^3 n^{1/2} \text{ cps}, \qquad (1\text{-}12)$$

for $n = 10^{14}$ per cm^3 and $\nu_\mathrm{p} = 9 \times 10^{10}$ per sec. Collisions between ions and electrons will tend to damp these collective oscillations. In order for the oscillations to be only slightly damped, the collision frequency ν_c must be so small that

$$\nu_\mathrm{p} \gg \nu_\mathrm{c}. \qquad (1\text{-}13)$$

This completes the list of conditions for a collection of charged particles to exhibit plasma-like behavior. The conditions can be summarized in terms of Eqs. 1-2, 1-3, 1-7, and 1-13. They are: $D \ll L$, the Debye length is small compared to the linear extent of the plasma; $\frac{4}{3}\pi n_e D^3 \gg 1$, there are many electrons in a Debye sphere; $n_i \approx n_e$, the plasma is approximately neutral; $\nu_p \gg \nu_c$, plasma oscillations are not strongly damped.

Sometimes the term *plasma physics* is applied to the study of systems of charged particles in which the collective effects do not necessarily play a dominant role. This extension of the use of the plasma designation has likely occurred because there are physical situations in which it is not yet possible to evaluate accurately the role of collective effects and because the independent-particle behavior often yields insight into plasma properties even when collective effects are important.

§ **1-2 Occurrence of Plasma.** Having discussed the conditions required of a plasma, we can now describe various systems and situations in which plasmas occur. These situations fall into three broad categories: various plasma devices such as "neon" lights that are in common use, laboratory plasmas that are used to investigate plasma properties and to develop devices such as thermonuclear fusion reactors, and cosmic plasmas that occur throughout most of the extraterrestrial universe.

From the discussion of the last section it is clear that a useful representation of a plasma can be made in terms of electron density and temperature, and quantities dependent upon them, the Debye shielding distance and the plasma frequency. Hence the various plasmas referred to above can be displayed as in Fig. 1-2 on a plot of electron density vs electron temperature. The wide variety of situations in which plasma plays a part is at once evident, and comparisons between plasmas of greatly differing parameters can be made. Perhaps the most familiar entry is an ordinary flame. In a flame the ionization energy is supplied by the oxidation of the fuel. Flames are seen to have an electron density around 10^8 per cm^3 and an electron temperature of about 2000–5000°K. These conditions yield a Debye shielding distance of 0.1 mm, which is small compared to the size of most flames. To see if the condition $D \gg (3/4\pi n_e)^{1/3}$ is satisfied we note that $D \approx 10^{-2}$ cm and $(1/n)^{1/3} \approx$

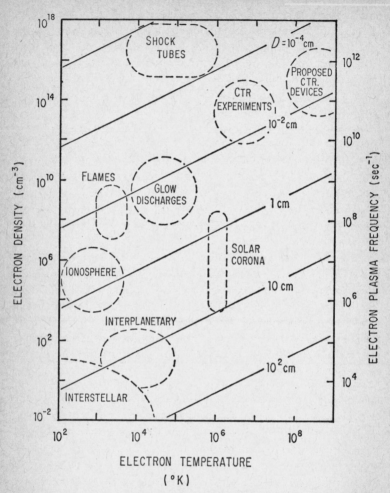

FIG. 1-2 Plasma parameters for a variety of laboratory and cosmic plasmas in terms of electron density and temperature. CTR refers to "controlled thermonuclear reaction."

2×10^{-3} cm. Thus a flame may be marginally considered to be a plasma although the number of electrons in a Debye sphere is only about 400.

Various types of experimental plasmas can be formed with

much higher densities and temperatures than are present in flames. Perhaps the most widely publicized of these laboratory plasmas are those used for thermonuclear fusion research. In these studies it is hoped that high temperature plasma of adequate density can be confined for appreciable times so that nuclear fusion reactions can occur among the constituent nuclei. The energy release from the fusion reactions could then provide a source of power.

Another type of plasma that we discuss in this book is that which occurs in the solar corona and in interplanetary and interstellar space. The solar corona decreases in density over several orders of magnitude in its extension to large distances from the sun. This plasma is seen to have a narrow temperature range in the vicinity of 10^6 °K. Interplanetary and interstellar plasma are much more dilute. The ionization energy for these plasmas comes from stellar radiations.

In Chapter 3 we shall consider laboratory plasmas under two of the categories shown in Fig. 1-2. These are the glow discharges that commonly have a rather low degree of ionization and the highly-ionized plasmas used in hydromagnetic and fusion experiments. In Chapter 4 we discuss the plasma of the solar corona, the interplanetary regions, and the interstellar plasma involved in galactic structures.

§ 1-3 The Particles in a Plasma. The collective motions in plasmas have been emphasized in § 1-1 because they distinguish plasmas from other groups of charged particles. However, these collective aspects by no means constitute the only useful way to think about a plasma. For a plasma in which collisions and other charged particle interactions are weak, certain features may be most easily understood in terms of independent particle motions. The purpose of this section is to review these motions as they are influenced by externally applied electric and magnetic fields. However, it must be realized that collective motions are important under most plasma conditions. Therefore, this treatment of independent motions, though capable of yielding considerable insight and useful in many circumstances, is not an alternative to the macroscopic discussion given in Chapter 2.

Although the primary concern here is with electrons and ions, a general particle of mass m and charge q is discussed first. Whenever it is useful to do so, these general properties will be replaced by electron and ion masses, m_e and m_i, respectively, and the unit charge $-e$ or e. Electric fields will be designated by E and magnetic fields by B. B rather than H is used throughout this book since B directly affects particle motion under all circumstances. By using it we avoid the explicit introduction of permeability into many equations.

The motion of a charged particle in a constant electric field is quite analogous to that of a mass particle in a gravitational field. In both cases a constant force acts upon the particle and can produce various constant acceleration trajectories. The simplest trajectory is a linear accelerated motion in the field direction for a particle starting from rest. The force equation for this motion in a constant E field is

$$m(dv/dt) = qE, \qquad (1\text{-}14)$$

where v is the particle velocity. For the case considered, v is parallel to E and increases at a uniform rate throughout the regions of constant E. When the particle starts with velocity v_0 rather than from rest, the component of v_0 parallel to E adds to the velocity achieved as a result of the accelerated motion. The components perpendicular to E remain constant since Eq. 1-14 becomes $m(dv/dt) = 0$ in those directions.

Charged particle motion in a constant magnetic field is somewhat more complicated. A force is exerted by the magnetic field only by virtue of the component of velocity lying perpendicular to the field direction. Thus the simplest situation involves an initial particle velocity perpendicular to the field. The magnetic field exerts a force given by qvB. Thus

$$m(dv/dt) = qvB, \qquad (1\text{-}15)$$

the acceleration dv/dt being always perpendicular to v and B in the direction indicated in Fig. 1-3. (If q is replaced by the electron charge $-e$, the force is, of course, directed opposite to that shown.) Since the magnitude of the force is constant and always perpendicular to v, the motion must be circular.

The acceleration required for circular motion with radius a is v^2/a, and this may be set equal to dv/dt from Eq. 1-15. Thus

$$v^2/a = qvB/m, \qquad (1\text{-}16)$$

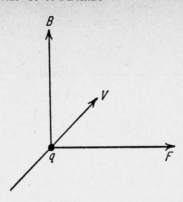

FIG. 1-3   Direction of force exerted on a particle of charge q by a constant magnetic field B.

and from this we find the angular frequency $\omega_c = v/a$ to be

$$\omega_c = qB/m. \tag{1-17}$$

This quantity is called the *cyclotron frequency;* its independence of v provides the physical mechanism for the design of low-energy cyclotrons. The radius of gyration a is given by

$$a = v/\omega_c = mv/qB. \tag{1-18}$$

For an initial velocity not perpendicular to B, the component parallel to B will persist unchanged, and the component perpendicular to B will be specified according to Eq. 1-15. The motion produced by this initial velocity takes the form of a helix of constant pitch. In a uniform magnetic field the particles gyrate at constant radius about a given field line. In a sense the particle is "locked" to this field line. In Chapter 2 we shall see the consequence of this effect when the plasma particles are considered as a conducting fluid.

Another important plasma effect occurs as a result of the combined effects of perpendicular electric and magnetic fields upon the charged particle motions. The cases considered here involve motions confined to a plane perpendicular to the direction of the magnetic field. Consider a particle moving at constant velocity v perpendicular to both B and E. The force exerted by E is in the direction of E and that exerted by B is perpendicular to B and hence parallel or antiparallel to E. When the magnitudes and directions of the fields and the velocity are such that the magnetic force is equal and opposite to the electric force, the particle will proceed undeflected. In this case, the required velocity can be calculated by equating the electric and magnetic forces:

$$Eq = Bqv. \qquad (1\text{-}19)$$

This velocity perpendicular to both E and B, called the *drift velocity*, is designated by v_D. From Eq. 1-19

$$v_D = E/B. \qquad (1\text{-}20)$$

More complicated results are obtained when the initial particle velocity is not equal to v_D or is not perpendicular to B. However, all of these cases may be described by particle gyration about the direction of B at an angular frequency given by Eq. 1-17, $\omega_c = qB/m$, superimposed upon a linear drift motion of velocity $v_D = E/B$. A trajectory of a positively charged particle in such combined fields is shown in Fig. 1-4. From this figure we see that as the particle

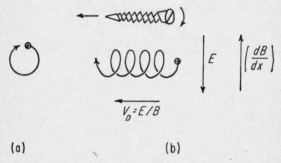

(a)   (b)

FIG. 1-4 Trajectory of a charged particle subject to the perpendicular electric and magnetic fields shown in the plane perpendicular to B.

moves against the electric field its velocity is decreased, with a corresponding decrease in radius of curvature. Then as the motion is accelerated by E the radius of curvature increases. The E field is seen to induce the drift motion to the left. The direction of this drift for positively charged particles is seen to be in the direction of advance of a right-handed screw when E is turned toward B.

Of course, the same type of drift will occur for another type of force field, such as gravity, that might replace E.

The same trajectory as that shown in Fig. 1-4 can be produced by a magnetic field alone. If the magnetic field intensity is larger at the top of the loops of the path than at the bottom, the radius of curvature will again be smallest at the top and largest at the bottom. The result of these changes in radius of curvature during particle motion is also to induce a particle drift to the right as shown.

For such a magnetic field the calculation of drift velocity is not simple and, in fact, can be carried out only approximately. The result of an approximate calculation is

$$v_D = \frac{mv^2}{2qB^2} \left(-\frac{dB}{dx} \right), \tag{1-21}$$

where v is the initial particle velocity. The drift velocity is perpendicular to B and to its space rate of change, dB/dx. The direction of this drift for positively charged particles is the direction of advance of a right-handed screw when the direction of decreasing B is turned toward B.

A very important and useful property of gyrating charged particles is the *magnetic moment*, which is defined as the product of the current due to the particle gyration multiplied by the area enclosed by that current. The utility of the magnetic moment μ derives from the fact that for slow variations of B either in space or time, μ is essentially constant. Thus the effects of such field variations may be treated by noting the consequences of requiring the constancy of μ.

The above definition of the magnetic moment can be written

$$\mu = (\pi a^2)(q\omega_c/2\pi). \tag{1-22}$$

The first bracket is the area enclosed by the particle motion; the second is the charge divided by the time required for one gyration.

An immediate consequence of Eq. 1-22 is that the magnetic moment is proportional to the flux $\phi = \pi a^2 B$ through the particle orbit. From Eqs. 1-22 and 1-17

$$\mu = \pi a^2 B(q^2/2\pi m) = (q^2/2\pi m)\phi. \tag{1-23}$$

Thus for conditions such that μ is constant, the flux within particle orbits will remain constant. Figure 1-5 shows the result of this requirement in a magnetic field that varies slowly with position. As the magnetic field lines converge, the particle orbit is compressed in such a way as to maintain ϕ constant. Therefore, the particle is seen to move along the surface of a flux tube.

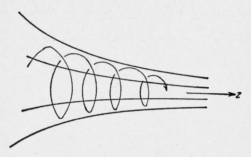

FIG. 1-5   Motion of a particle in a magnetic field that varies slowly with position.

To show the constancy of μ with respect to a varying magnetic field we start with Faraday's law, which equates the induced electromotive force $\mathcal{E}$ around a closed path to the rate of change of flux $d\phi/dt$ within the path. Thus

$$\mathcal{E} = \frac{d\phi}{dt} = \pi r^2 \frac{dB}{dt}. \qquad (1\text{-}24)$$

When the change in field is negligibly small, the work done upon a particle of charge q in one orbit is $q\mathcal{E}$ and equals dW/dt times the period of one orbit, $2\pi/\omega_c$, and we have from Eq. 1-24:

$$\frac{2\pi}{\omega_c}\left(\frac{dW}{dt}\right) = \frac{2\pi}{\omega_c}\frac{dW}{dB}\left(\frac{dB}{dt}\right) = q\pi r^2 \frac{dB}{dt}. \qquad (1\text{-}25)$$

If the change in B during one orbit is negligibly small compared to B, then $r = a$. From Eq. 1-25 and Eq. 1-22

$$\frac{dW}{dB} = (\pi a^2)\left(\frac{q\omega_c}{2\pi}\right) = \mu. \qquad (1\text{-}26)$$

The work done is equal to the particle kinetic energy. Then

$$W = \tfrac{1}{2}mv^2 = \tfrac{1}{2}m\omega_c^2 a^2 = \mu B \qquad (1\text{-}27)$$

from Eqs. 1-17, 1-18, and 1-22. Differentiating Eq. 1-27 with respect to B,

$$\frac{dW}{dB} = \frac{d(\mu B)}{dB} = B\frac{d\mu}{dB} + \mu, \qquad (1\text{-}28)$$

which from Eq. 1-26 must equal μ. Therefore $d\mu/dB = 0$, and μ is a constant independent of B.

The above proof is valid for magnetic fields which vary slowly enough so that the change of field over one particle orbit is negligibly small compared to the field value.

Of course, if the magnetic field is modulated sinusoidally at an angular frequency equal to ω_c, this requirement is clearly not satisfied, and the magnetic moment does not remain constant. In such a case, a resonance condition exists, and the particles can extract large amounts of energy from the field modulation.

For particles moving in fields like that shown in Fig. 1-5, the converging field acts like a mirror and can reflect some particles. To see this effect, we rewrite Eq. 1-27 in the form

$$\mu = \tfrac{1}{2}mv^2/B = W_\perp/B \qquad (1\text{-}29)$$

Here $W_\perp$ is the kinetic energy due to the velocity v that is perpendicular to B. The component of velocity parallel to B will carry the particles along the field lines in the z direction. An energy $W_\parallel$ can be associated with this motion. Conservation of energy requires that the total energy

$$W = W_\perp + W_\parallel \qquad (1\text{-}30)$$

be a constant.

The reflection of particles by the *magnetic "mirror"* is a consequence of this energy requirement. As particles move into regions of higher B, constancy of μ implies a corresponding increase of $W_\perp$. This energy increase can only occur at the expense of $W_\parallel$, and the particle is thus slowed in its motion in the z direction. The particle is stopped and reflected at the point where $W_\parallel = 0$ and $W = W_\perp$. At this turning point $\mu = W/B$, and particles for which $W < \mu B$ will be reflected. Using Eq. 1-29, this reflection condition becomes

$$W/W_\perp(0) < B_{max}/B(0), \qquad (1\text{-}31)$$

where $W_\perp(0)$ and $B(0)$ are the values of $W_\perp$ and B at a region away from the converging magnetic field and where B_{max} is the maximum mirror field. To be reflected, the particles must have velocity components perpendicular to the field large enough to satisfy Eq. 1-31.

§ **1-4 Particle Interactions.** The individual particle motions considered thus far have been produced by forces resulting from externally applied fields. We now turn our attention to individual particle interactions with other particles. These interactions form the basis for the kinetic properties and macroscopic behavior of plasma to be discussed in the next chapter.

As we noted earlier, there is great variety to the particle interactions that occur in a plasma. These interactions are generally divided into two types: elastic and inelastic. We first consider elastic collisions. During such collisions the interacting particles remain unchanged in internal energy and constitution. The collision or scattering thus conserves energy and momentum, and only the particle velocities are altered. An example of an elastic collision is the so-called hard-sphere interaction that provides an approximate description of neutral-atom collisions.

Two neutral atoms may approach within a very short distance of each other before any forces become appreciable. Only for interatomic distances so small that the interaction perturbs the orbital electrons does the electron repulsion begin to act. When it does, the force increases very rapidly with decreasing distance. Since the force and the potential energy to which it is related is such a steep function of separation, it is often replaced by an approximation. For separation distances beyond that for which the interaction force has just begun to act, the force is taken equal to zero; inside this distance the force is taken to be infinite. In this way the actual interatomic force is approximated by that which would arise if the atoms were hard spheres. Many characteristics of neutral gases may be accounted for on the basis of this hard-sphere approximation to the neutral-particle collision.

Because of its simplicity the hard-sphere model will be used initially to discuss collision probabilities. Later the discussion will be broadened to include a more general form of particle interaction. Consider a "hard-sphere" particle of radius r_1 incident upon a randomly distributed group of "hard-sphere" particles of radius r_2 as shown in Fig. 1-6. A collision occurs if the center of

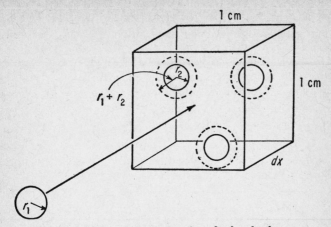

FIG. 1-6 Scattering cross sections for hard spheres.

particle 1 comes within a distance $(r_1 + r_2)$ of the center of any one of the group of particles of radius r_2. The density of the latter particles is taken as N per cm³. The total cross sectional area presented per cm² for a thickness dx of the scatterers is $N\pi(r_1 + r_2)^2\, dx$.

Since one of a group of incident particles is as likely to pass along any path through the group of scatterers, the fraction of particles depleted from the incident group by collisions in the distance dx is

$$dn/n = -N\pi(r_1 + r_2)^2\, dx. \qquad (1\text{-}32)$$

Here dn/n expresses the fractional change in the number of incident particles per cm² and is negative because the scattering does deplete the incident particle density. Integration of Eq. 1-32 yields

$$n = n_0 \exp\left[-N\pi(r_1 + r_2)^2 x\right], \qquad (1\text{-}33)$$

where n_0 is the incident particle density at $x = 0$.

The quantity $\pi(r_1 + r_2)^2$ is seen to have the units of area and is called the cross section for hard-sphere scattering. We may now generalize the foregoing discussion by retaining the form of Eq. 1-33 and replacing the specific hard-sphere cross section by a general interaction cross section σ. Then if we consider a unit area of scatterers perpendicular to a particle beam direction x, the density decrease of the beam in traversing the distance dx of the scatterer is given from Eq. 1-32 as

$$dn = -nN\sigma \, dx, \tag{1-34}$$

where σ is the scattering cross section. Integration yields

$$n = n_0 \exp(-N\sigma x), \tag{1-35}$$

where n_0 is the beam density at $x = 0$. One interpretation of Eq. 1-35 is that $\exp(-N\sigma x)$ is the probability that a particle will go a distance x without suffering a scattering. With this probability a mean scattering or collision length $\langle x_c \rangle$ can be obtained from

$$\langle x_c \rangle = \int_0^\infty nx \, dx \Big/ \int_0^\infty n \, dx,$$

and the result is

$$\langle x_c \rangle = 1/N\sigma. \tag{1-36}$$

Yet another useful quantity is the mean scattering or collision frequency ν_c, which is directly related to $\langle x_c \rangle$ through the particle speed v by

$$\nu_c = v/\langle x_c \rangle = vN\sigma. \tag{1-37}$$

To have in mind the order of magnitudes of σ, $\langle x_c \rangle$, and ν_c, we evaluate these for collision of hydrogen atoms with hydrogen atom scatterers, assuming a hard-sphere interaction with $R = r_1 + r_2 = 1.8 \times 10^{-8}$ cm. This yields $\sigma \approx 10^{-15}$ cm². For hydrogen at 10^{-5} atmospheric pressure, $N \approx 5 \times 10^{14}$ cm⁻³. Thus $\langle x_c \rangle = 2$ cm. For a hydrogen beam of one eV, energy $v \approx 6 \times 10^4$ cm/sec, and $\nu_c = 3 \times 10^4$ sec⁻¹.

For collisions that cannot be approximated by hard spheres the determination of σ is much more complex. An important aspect of the complication is that these cross sections are not generally energy independent as for the hard-sphere approximation. For scattering of charged particles by charged particles the cross section is proportional to $1/W^2$, where W is the kinetic energy of the scattered particle.

Passage of charged particles in the vicinity of neutral atoms will cause a temporary distortion of the electronic configuration of the atoms. A positively charged particle near a neutral atom will tend to attract the atomic electrons toward the side on which it passes, and a net attractive force is exerted because of this polarization of the neutral atom. This attractive force will increase the scattering cross section above that for hard-sphere scattering. Since the degree of polarization will depend upon the time spent by the charged particle in the vicinity of the neutral atom, the polarization cross section is also expected to be energy dependent and is proportional to $W^{-1/2}$.

Inelastic collisions are unlike those discussed above in that the energy and/or internal constitution of the interacting particles are changed as a result of the collision. Such collisions are important because plasma production and decay processes are largely dominated by them.

Atoms are excited or ionized as the atomic electrons acquire sufficient energy to be raised above their lowest energy state or to be freed from the atom, respectively. The energy to produce excitation or ionization may be added in many ways. Two predominant modes involve electron and photon collisions which can efficiently add energy to atomic electrons. The large mass ratio of ions and electrons makes ions much less effective in producing ionization or excitation. Only when incident particle velocities approach those of the orbital electrons can excitations occur, and these velocities correspond to an energy of about 10^3 eV for ions. Few plasma systems contain ions of these energies. For electrons, the excitation and ionization cross sections increase rapidly with energy when the energy is adequate to produce either process. Both cross sections pass through broad maxima and then decrease as the time spent in the vicinity of the atom becomes too short for effective energy interchange. Electron ionization cross sections are as large as 10^{-16} cm^2 in hydrogen.

Photon excitation and ionization may occur whenever the photon energy equals that required for excitation and equals or exceeds that needed for ionization. In each of these cases the entire photon energy is transferred to the atom-electron system. Any excess over that required for ionization is thus largely carried away by the released electron. Photon ionization cross sections may be as high as 10^{-16} cm^2.

Electrons can be exchanged during collisions of ions and atoms. Such interactions are called charge-exchange or charge-transfer processes. These processes have much larger cross sections than those for excitation or ionization and may range up to 10^{-15} or 10^{-14} cm^2. Charge-exchange processes are important in partially ionized plasmas and in situations where neutral impurity atoms may be present. Then ions can be lost from magnetically confined plasmas after being neutralized during charge-exchange collisions.

Two other deionization processes are important in the plasmas considered later in this book. These processes are radiative and three-body recombination. In very dilute plasmas where particle interactions are quite infrequent, most recombination occurs by electron capture by an ion with the emitted photons taking the released energy. Most cosmic plasmas recombine predominantly in this manner.

In denser plasmas, recombination is aided by the presence of a neighboring second electron which is not captured but which can ease the momentum conservation requirements of the captured electron. The decay of many laboratory plasmas is observed to proceed by this three-body process.

§ 1-5 **Particle Distributions.** Nearly all of the processes treated in the preceding sections are dependent upon the velocity or kinetic energy of the interacting particles. In a plasma all particles do not have the same velocity, but are distributed over a considerable range of values. The situation in a gaseous plasma is something like that in an ordinary gas except that in a plasma the free electrons are also able to move about independently. Thermo-dynamic equilibrium for a plasma, as for an ordinary gas, requires that the thermal and other physical variables of the system remain essentially constant over times of significance to the behavior of the system. In an ordinary gas in thermodynamic equilibrium the molecular velocities v follow a so-called Maxwell-Boltzmann distribution

$$p(v) = v^2 \left(\frac{m}{2\pi kT} \right)^{3/2} \exp\left(-\frac{mv^2}{2kT} \right), \qquad (1\text{-}38)$$

in which $p(v)$ expresses the relative number of particles of velocity v. The temperature T is seen to provide a measure of the distribution of particle velocities. In Eq. 1-38 m is the particle mass, and k is the Boltzmann constant.

It is very hard to find a plasma in complete thermodynamic equilibrium. Various excitation, de-excitation, and particle loss processes prevent such an equilibrium from occurring. However, in many circumstances the condition of a plasma is near enough to equilibrium so that the distribution function expressed by Eq. 1-38 can hold rather accurately. When Eq. 1-38 holds, a thermodynamic temperature may be defined for the plasma particles.

Sometimes the velocity distributions of ions and electrons of a plasma differ appreciably. If for some reason each species is in a state of quasi-equilibrium, then appropriate temperatures may be defined for the ions and electrons separately. Such temperature differences can be maintained on a steady state basis only when external energies are supplied in such a way as to maintain the difference.

Since the particles of a plasma are distributed in velocity, all of the particle interactions discussed earlier in this chapter must be affected by the distribution. Thus a particular property of a plasma is determined by a complicated averaging of the various velocity-dependent interactions over the spectrum of velocities present in the plasma.

When a plasma is not in thermodynamic equilibrium over its entire extent, it is sometimes possible to specify certain portions that are in thermodynamic equilibrium. When this is possible, many of the procedures that are applicable to an equilibrium analysis, including assignment of a temperature, can be made over the regions where equilibrium holds.

For a plasma in equilibrium at a temperature T it is possible to deduce the relative populations of the excited and ionization states of the plasma ions. The original calculation was made by Saha, and the resulting equilibrium state population equation is usually given his name. The derivation of the *Saha equation* for hydrogen can be made in a straightforward manner, but it will only be outlined here.

The electron of a hydrogen atom may be in any one of many states. The lowest states are shown in the simplified energy-level diagram, Fig. 1-7. For all electron energies below $W = 0$ the electron is bound to the ion, and for energies $W > 0$ the electrons are free and the atom is ionized. The ionization potential is the energy that must be added to an electron to raise it from the lowest ($n = 1$) level to $W = 0$. To calculate the relative numbers of ionized and neutral atoms in hydrogen at a particular temperature,

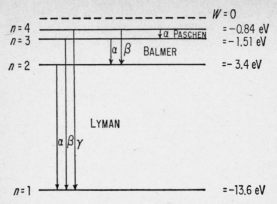

FIG. 1-7 Simplified energy-level diagram for hydrogen.

it is necessary to use a distribution function similar to that given by Eq. 1-38. The situation is somewhat different because of the necessarily quantum-mechanical aspects of the atomic problem. In this case the probability P_n that a quantum mechanical system having discrete energy levels W_n is in the nth state is

$$P_n = g_n e^{-W_n/kT}/Z_b, \tag{1-39}$$

where g_n is called the statistical weight of the nth state, W_n is the state energy, and Z_b is a normalizing function chosen so that the total probability summed over all bound states is one. The statistical weight is given by the number of substates within the state n. It is likewise possible to write the corresponding probability for the free electrons. When these probabilities are combined, one finds that

$$\frac{n_i n_e}{n_n} = \frac{2g_i}{g_n} \frac{(2\pi m_e kT)^{3/2}}{h^3} \exp\left(-X_n/kT\right), \tag{1-40}$$

where n_i, n_e, and n_n are the ion, electron, and nth state densities, respectively; g_i and g_n are the ion and nth state statistical weights, respectively; h is Planck's constant; and X_n is the ionization energy of the nth state. This is Saha's equation for hydrogen. It gives the number density ratios between ions, electrons, and neutrals in various excitation states. It turns out to be unnecessary to determine Z_b since in the ratio formed in Eq. 1-40 it cancels out. We see that at very high temperatures the exponential becomes unity and the ratio $n_i n_e / n_n$ increases as $T^{3/2}$. That is, as the temperature increases, so does the percentage ionization, a not surprising result.

It is evident from Eq. 1-40 that for a plasma at a given temperature there exists a definite distribution of atoms at various states of excitations and ionization. As long as there is a balance between all the populating and depopulating influences upon a particular state, this statistical distribution will hold, and the plasma is said to be in local thermodynamic equilibrium.

2 *Plasma as a Conducting Fluid and Wave-Propagating Medium*

The properties of a plasma can in principle be accounted for by summing up the individual contributions made by all the particles and their interactions. As a practical matter this procedure is difficult. For a general insight, a macroscopic approach is often more useful.

In the macroscopic treatment one discusses a small volume of plasma that is large compared to the average spacings of the individual particles it contains, yet small compared to any distances over which the macroscopic plasma properties vary appreciably. To this volume of plasma are given the average values of velocity, magnetic field, density, temperature, pressure, conductivity, etc., appropriate to that volume. Then the behavior of the plasma as a whole is deduced in terms of the actions of all these small volumes into which the plasma is divided.

This technique of treating macroscopic elements of a system as entities that can possess such average properties is familiar in the treatment of electromagnetic and hydrodynamic phenomena. Indeed, a substantial part of the discussion in this chapter will have much in common with both of these fields of physics and is actually a combination of the two. The result, called *magnetohydrodynamics* or *hydromagnetics*, is the treatment of a conducting fluid subject simultaneously to the laws of electromagnetics and hydrodynamics.

The sets of laws that apply to either electromagnetics or hydrodynamics are not particularly simple, but in each case the essential consequences are reasonably well understood. The prime business of this chapter is to deal with certain combinations of electromagnetic and hydromagnetic effects. Obviously, these combinations can be very complicated, so we limit the discussion to a few simple situations that are illustrative of the general phenomena.

In addition to strictly hydromagnetic effects we shall also discuss certain types of plasma wave motions in this chapter; § 2-3 contains a discussion of electromagnetic and hydromagnetic waves in plasma.

§ **2-1 Magnetic Field Effects.** To understand the effects of a magnetic field upon a conducting fluid it is useful to consider first the related effects produced on rigid conductors. In metallic conductors electricity is carried solely by the electrons, some of which are free to move relative to the bound atoms and ions making up the lattice of the solid. Although this situation differs from that found in a plasma where atomic, ionic, and electronic components are free to move, the initial discussion of solid conductors provides a helpful introduction.

Let a conducting wire of length l be placed perpendicular to a magnetic field B and let it be drawn at velocity v perpendicular to both the field B and the length of the wire, as in Fig. 2-1. The particles of charge q in the conductor are acted upon by the force

$$F = Bqv. \qquad (2-1)$$

The electrons which are free to move will respond to this force and migrate toward the left-hand end of the wire. The increased density

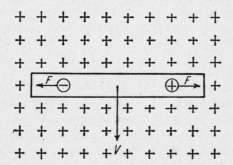

FIG. 2-1 Forces acting on the electrons and positive nuclei in a wire moving perpendicular to a magnetic field directed into the page.

of electrons at the left and their corresponding decreased density at the right will build up until the electric field E produced by the charge separation is large enough to equal the magnetic force given by Eq. 2-1. Then $Eq = -Bqv$, the minus sign reflecting the right-handed coordinate sign convention of Fig. 1-4. The electric potential V across the wire is

$$V = El = -Bvl. \tag{2-2}$$

Since vl is the area perpendicular to B swept over by the wire per unit time, Bvl is the time rate of change of the magnetic flux ϕ, and the induced potential is

$$V = -(d\phi/dt). \tag{2-3}$$

If a closed conducting loop is placed within a magnetic field, the electromotive force (emf) induced around the loop is given by *Faraday's induction law*. This electromotive force $\mathcal{E}$ equals the negative of the time rate of change of flux through the loop. The current I which flows in such a loop as a result of the induced emf is determined by the resistance R of the loop. Thus

$$\mathcal{E} = -(d\phi/dt) = IR. \tag{2-4}$$

In the special case in which the loop resistance R is zero, we note the interesting consequence that the induced emf and hence the time rate of change of flux $d\phi/dt$ must vanish. This result is simply a limiting case of the well-known Lenz's rule, which states that when the flux linking a closed circuit is changing, the flux set up by the induced current is in such a direction as to tend to prevent the change in flux.

The above ideas may be extended to a conducting fluid, in which case also

$$d\phi/dt = 0 \tag{2-5}$$

through any surface moving with a fluid of zero resistivity. This means that the magnetic flux through any surface in the fluid tends to remain constant as that surface moves about with the fluid motions. This concept of constant flux may be extended, subject to certain restrictions, to provide that the elements of a fluid of negligible resistivity are "frozen" to the magnetic lines of force. Or more commonly, and equivalently, it is often said that the lines of force are "frozen in" the conducting fluid and are thereby constrained to move with the fluid.

The concept of "frozen-in" fields is important to hydromagnetic discussions of plasma since it provides an easy means of visualizing the interplay between the conducting plasma and the field. If we imagine an element of the plasma to undergo displacement, change of shape, and even change in density, the magnetic flux through the element will remain constant.

Of course, if the resistivity is not zero, some motion of the field lines with respect to the plasma is possible. Thus in reality the field is not exactly constrained to follow the plasma motion. Although it tends to be so restrained, it will slip slowly through the plasma. The rate at which a magnetic field threading a plasma can change equals that for the diffusion of a plasma across a magnetic field and is fixed by the resistivity and dimensions of the plasma. The rate may be calculated approximately by noting that plasma motion across field lines will induce currents to flow. Analogously to Eqs. 2-4 and 2-2, these current densities j are given by

$$\eta j = vB, \tag{2-6}$$

where η is the plasma resistivity. These currents which flow perpendicular to B will produce, in concert with the magnetic field, a force jB upon the various plasma elements. If no other forces act and if there is no turbulence, this force will equal that due to gradients in the plasma pressure ∇p perpendicular to B, and from Eq. 2-6

$$v = (\nabla p/B^2)\eta. \tag{2-7}$$

Approximate values of the *diffusion time* τ for motion of the plasma across the field may be obtained from dimensional arguments using Eq. 2-7. Setting $v = L/\tau$, where L is a linear dimension of the plasma, and $\nabla p = p/L = nkT/L$, where n and T are plasma density and temperature, respectively, and k is the Boltzmann constant, we have

$$\tau = L^2 \left(\frac{B^2}{nkT} \right) \frac{1}{\eta}. \tag{2-8}$$

Table 2-1 lists values of the diffusion time for magnetic fields in various conducting materials calculated from Eq. 2-8.

TABLE 2-1 *Approximate diffusion times for magnetic fields in various materials.*

	Size L (cm)	Resistivity (ohm-cm)	Diffusion Time (sec)
Copper	10	1.7×10^{-8}	1
Laboratory plasma ($T = 1$ eV)	10	10^{-3}	10^{-5}
Thermonuclear plasma ($T = 10$ keV)	100	10^{-9}	10^{3}
Sun spot ($T = 0.5$ eV)	10^{9}	10^{-2}	10^{10} (100 yrs)
Earth's core	3×10^{8}	10^{-5}	10^{12} (10^{4} yrs)

Inferences concerning the nature of sun spots and of the geomagnetic field may be drawn from Table 2-1. The diffusion time given for sun spots yields ample evidence that processes other than those used to deduce Eq. 2-8 quite likely operate on the surface of the sun. Sun spots, as indicated in § 4-1, are highly dominated by magnetic fields, yet their observed lifetimes are generally something like two orders of magnitude less than the diffusion times calculated from Eq. 2-8. Various types of hydromagnetic turbulence and instability can provide alternate and faster movement of plasma with respect to the magnetic fields in which they are immersed. More details of these instabilities are given in § 2-2.

The diffusion time given for the earth's core represents an upper limit to the time that some primordial field could have lasted. Since this time is short compared to 10^{9} years, which is the approximate age of the earth, the geomagnetic field must be continuously regenerated. Some type of self-sustaining dynamo action of the conducting fluid core is thought to be the most likely regeneration mechanism although no completely satisfactory proof to support such a proposal has yet been given.

The above macroscopic discussion of the diffusion of plasma in magnetic fields skirts around the role that the plasma particles play. However, this aspect is easily recovered. Any calculation or discussion of the resistivity η, which appears in Eq. 2-8, must be made in terms of particle motions. It is easy to see qualitatively how the particle motions can result in the "frozen-in" field condition if the resistivity is zero.

The resistivity of any conducting material is due to interparticle collisions within the material. In the absence of such collisions the particles of the material can respond unhindered to applied electric or magnetic fields. Thus the electrons and ions of a zero-resistivity, collisionless plasma will be constrained to spiral about the magnetic field lines in which the plasma is immersed. With no collisions to disrupt this motion, the particles and the plasma as a whole cannot move with respect to the field.

However, if collisions occur, the resistivity no longer is zero, and the collisions cause the particles to be scattered as they encircle the field lines. The random nature of this scattering allows the orbiting particles to be attached sequentially to various field lines and thus diffuse across the magnetic field. Crucial to the plasma behavior under these circumstances is the ratio of the collision frequency to the cyclotron frequencies of the ions and electrons.

Under most circumstances the electrical conducting properties of a material are largely dependent upon the low mass, highly mobile electrons. Thus the resistivity usually depends primarily upon the electron collision effects. Since the collision frequency depends upon the collision cross sections and upon the thermal agitation of the conducting electrons, the resistivity is similarly dependent. Over relatively wide ranges of density and temperature the relevant cross sections do not modify the resistivity strongly, and the temperature dependence may be separated out. In a plasma the collision frequency decreases with increasing temperature, and thus the electrical resistivity decreases. This temperature dependence is opposite to that in ordinary conductors. For a hydrogen plasma the resistivity works out to be

$$\eta = \frac{9.5 \times 10^{-2}}{T_e^{3/2}} \text{ ohm-cm}, \tag{2-9}$$

where T_e is the electron temperature in eV. Representative values of the resistivity of various materials are given in Table 2-1.

Of course, if a magnetic field is applied to a plasma, the resistivity across the field lines will be larger than is given by Eq. 2-9; but along field lines the resistivity is not altered.

We noted above in connection with Eq. 2-7 that motion of plasma perpendicular to a magnetic field generates currents which interact with the field and cause the plasma to be subjected to a force of magnitude jB perpendicular to both j and B. The particular case discussed above was limited to motions and currents perpendicular to B. Although it is by no means obvious, it turns out that when this limitation is removed the resulting forces can be thought of as the sum of two components dependent only upon B. One component is equivalent to a hydrostatic pressure of magnitude $B^2/8\pi$ acting on the plasma. The other component is equivalent to a tension $B^2/4\pi$ acting along the magnetic lines. Thus the net effects of a magnetic field acting on a plasma may often be considered as a modification of the ordinary particle pressure by addition of $B^2/8\pi$ and addition of a tension $B^2/4\pi$ along the field. Figure 2-2

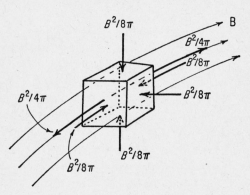

FIG. 2-2 Equivalent hydrostatic pressure and tension forces acting on a plasma in a magnetic field.

shows how these forces act upon an element of plasma volume. Although no proof is given here, the quadratic dependence on B of both these force terms is not surprising since the induced currents are proportional to B (from Eq. 2-6) and the forces are proportional to the current and B.

Any plasma motion that does not change the plasma density does not cause work to be done by the magnetic pressure $B^2/8\pi$. Hence any changes in total magnetic energy are then reflected as changes in the tension term $B^2/4\pi$. Stretching the field lines causes work to be done against this tension, and the magnetic energy is thereby increased. On the other hand, for field lines that are straight and parallel any changes in particle pressure p are compensated by corresponding changes in the magnetic pressure such that the total pressure is

$$p + (B^2/8\pi) = \text{a constant.} \tag{2-10}$$

A plasma at pressure p_1 may be "confined" by a magnetic field B_1 to a particular region even though surrounded by regions at a lower pressure p_2. This "confinement" from motion across B is evident from Eq. 2-10 when it is written in the form

$$p_1 + (B_1^2/8\pi) = p_2 + (B_2^2/8\pi). \tag{2-11}$$

When $B_2^2 > B_1^2$, confinement is possible even though $p_2 = 0$. We see from the inequality $B_1^2 < B_2^2$ that a plasma confined by a magnetic field behaves diamagnetically. That is, the field within the plasma is less than that in the surrounding space. Of course, only motion across the field lines is retarded by the magnetic field; for straight, parallel field lines the plasma is free to move along the lines. Confinement along field lines can be aided by use of magnetic mirrors as discussed in § 1-4. However, such fields decrease radially so that the condition $B_2^2 > B_1^2$ cannot be satisfied unless the plasma magnetic fields appreciably affect the inequality.

A specific example of plasma confinement occurs in the *pinch effect*. For purposes of illustration, consider a plasma of low resistivity to form a column of radius a carrying the current I, as shown in Fig. 2-3a. This current will produce a magnetic field

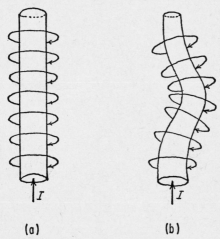

(a)   (b)

FIG. 2-3 The pinch effect on a plasma showing the equilibrium (a) and kink instability (b) of the column.

circling the column as shown. If the column boundaries are to be in equilibrium, the difference between the magnetic pressure outside the boundary and inside the column must equal the particle pressure inside. To the extent that the interior field is small compared to that on the outside, Eq. 2-11 yields

$$[B^2/8\pi]_{\text{outside}} = P_{\text{inside}} = nkT, \qquad (2\text{-}12)$$

where n is the total particle density. At the column boundary $B_a = 2I/a$, and Eq. 2-12 becomes

$$I^2/\pi a^2 = 2nkT. \qquad (2\text{-}13)$$

For a plasma of density $n = 6 \times 10^{15}$ cm^{-3}, $P_{\text{inside}} = 6 \times 10^{15} \times 1.6 \times 10^{-7} = 10^9$ dynes/cm^2. From Eq. 2-12 this pressure, $B^2/8\pi = 10^9$, which corresponds to about 1000 atmospheres, can be produced by a magnetic field $B = 1.6 \times 10^5$ gauss. From Eq. 2-13 such a field is produced by a current of 8×10^6 amps flowing in the column in Fig. 2-3a with the radius $a = 10$ cm. Thus this plasma current is expected to produce a magnetic field which is adequate to confine the plasma to this radius.

The plasma column is in a state of unstable equilibrium. If a small displacement of the column like that shown in Fig. 2-3b should occur, the kinks so formed will continue to develop. This kink instability grows because the magnetic pressure $B^2/8\pi$ is increased on the concave side and weakened on the opposite side. This inequality of *magnetic pressure* causes the kink to grow without limit until the column is disrupted. This and other examples of plasma instabilities will be discussed in the next section.

§ 2-2 **Instabilities.** The kink instability of the plasma pinch shown in Fig. 2-3 is an example of a large class of instability phenomena that is important to the dynamics of plasma. Most instabilities involve the collective motions of the plasma particles, and they can usually be described in terms of the conducting fluid model used in this chapter.

Instabilities are important in a wide range of physical situations in which plasmas play a part. Particularly well studied are the effects of instabilities on proposed schemes for the confinement of high temperature plasmas in controlled thermonuclear fusion devices. In these devices various arrangements of electric and magnetic fields are used in an attempt to heat and confine the plasma in such a manner as to cause fusion reactions to occur between the nuclei in the plasma. One influence which can disrupt the operation of these devices is the lack of stability of the confined plasma. In this section several types of instability that affect these and other plasmas are described.

The effects of instabilities upon the evolution of astrophysical systems are much less well known. Such instabilities undoubtedly occur and are crucial to the behavior of these systems. However, except in a few instances the observational evidence is too incomplete to allow more than a guess as to their effects. A few such instances are described in Chapter 4.

The stability or instability of any physical system is determined by its kinetic and potential energy as a function of the system parameters. Figure 2-4 represents two simple cases of a ball at rest: at a minimum of potential energy in Fig. 2-4a and at a maximum

(a)   (b)

FIG. 2-4   A ball at points of stable (a) and unstable (b) equilibrium.

in Fig. 2-4b. The ball at the potential energy minimum is in a stable configuration; we note that at any other position than the one shown the potential energy is increased. Since the kinetic energy is zero and cannot decrease, other positions are energetically impossible. The stability of the position shown can be tested in another manner. If the ball is perturbed slightly by pushing it up the side of the depression and releasing it, the ball will oscillate about the position shown regardless of the release point.

Each of these techniques can be used to show that the ball in Fig. 2-4b is in unstable equilibrium. For any position other than that shown the kinetic energy can be increased at the expense of the potential energy, and all positions are energetically possible. Or if the ball is perturbed by a displacement from the position shown, the displacement will continue to increase.

These two techniques are widely used to test the stability of physical systems and have been particularly useful in determining plasma stability for certain situations. However, the procedure is often complicated. The complications arise, of course, because of the involved dependence of either the energy or a perturbation parameter upon the other parameters of the system. Thus stability calculations tend to be among the most complex of plasma physics although the fundamental physical content is no more sophisticated than in the above discussion of Fig. 2-4. Because of this complexity, this section describes only those instabilities that can be given a degree of credibility without recourse to detailed analysis.

Returning to the plasma pinch shown in Fig. 2-3, we note that the pinch can be in equilibrium. However, any displacement of the plasma column from its equilibrium position will lead to increased displacement due to the resulting imbalance of the magnetic forces. A corresponding energy discussion could also be given for the pinch in which it is shown that increased displacements of the column lead to decreased potential energy for the system. In any case, since spontaneous displacements will occur in physical systems, plasma pinches are expected to be susceptible to the kink instabilities, and they are observed to be so.

A more general class of instabilities goes by one of the generic adjectives of *ripple*, *Taylor*, *flute*, or *interchange instability* depending upon the special situations in which it occurs. To consider these instabilities we begin by discussing the case of a plasma-vacuum interface that is subject to a magnetic field parallel to the interface and a force field perpendicular to it. This situation is shown in Fig. 2-5. The plane interface in Fig. 2-5a is in equilibrium; there are no forces tending to disturb it. However, we shall see that when the surface is disturbed by, for example, the sinusoidal perturbation in Fig. 2-5b, the equilibrium is unstable. Of course, the sinusoidal perturbation shown is of a special form, but any arbitrary disturbance can be represented by a summation of harmonic contributions such as that shown.

In § 1-3 we saw that charged particles subject to a magnetic field and some other perpendicular force field have a drift velocity perpendicular to both field directions given by $v_D = E/B$ in the case of an electric field or $v_D = mg/qB$ for a gravity field g. The

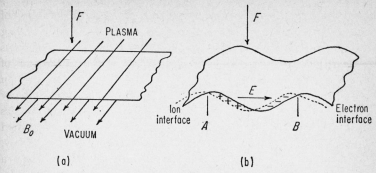

FIG. 2-5   Ripple instability at a vacuum-plasma interface before (a) and after (b) perturbation.

direction of the drift for the positive ions is, as before, given by the direction of advance of a right-handed screw when the force field F is turned toward B. Thus the drift velocity causes the ions of the plasma to move to the left and the electrons to the right in Fig. 2-5. When there is no perturbation, there is thus a continual flow of ions and electrons from and to the infinite extent of the plasma to the right and left of that shown. However, when the perturbation is present, these opposite drift motions produce a charge separation, and the electron and ion boundaries of the plasma are slightly displaced as in Fig. 2-5b.

It is obvious that these charge separations produce electric fields at the plasma-vacuum interface that have components which are parallel to the interface. In particular, between the positions A and B the separation field is toward the right. This field direction, in concert with the magnetic field B_0, produces a drift motion in the same direction as the original perturbation and thereby causes it to grow. Plasma in the region between A and B intrudes further into the vacuum region. If the force field F were opposite to that shown, the charge particle displacements would be reversed. The resultant drift motion would then oppose the original perturbation, and it would not grow. The growth of a displacement δ is given by

$$\delta(t) \propto \exp\left(\pm^t\sqrt{2\pi b/\lambda}\right), \qquad (2\text{-}14)$$

where λ is the wavelength of the perturbation and b is the strength of the force field. The sign and magnitude of b are determined by the direction and type of the force field F. When the direction of the force F is as shown in Fig. 2-5, b is positive, the exponent is real, and the displacement will grow; when it is oppositely directed, b is negative, the exponent is imaginary, and $\delta(t)$ is oscillatory.

If F is due to a gravity field, then $b = g$ and Eq. 2-14 gives the same result as is obtained for an ordinary dense fluid supported by a light fluid in a gravity field. In the case of such fluids, the motion caused by the dense fluid penetrating into the underlying light one is called a Taylor instability. For a gravity field in the plasma case, the electric charge does not appear in Eq. 2-14 because it happens that the effects of charge separation are just balanced by the restraining influence of the magnetic field.

In connection with Eq. 1-21 and Fig. 1-4 we saw that drift motions were also produced by spatially changing magnetic field intensities. For such magnetic fields the positive particle-drift direction is that determined by the direction of advance of a right-handed screw when the direction of decreasing B is turned into B. Figure 2-6 shows examples of such inhomogeneous magnetic fields.

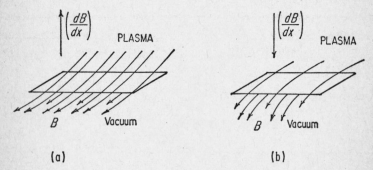

FIG. 2-6   A plasma-vacuum interface subject to a spacially variable magnetic field.

In Fig. 2-6a the field intensity is decreasing downward. The drift motions will be in the same direction as in Fig. 2-5, and the interface will likewise be unstable. In Fig. 2-6b the magnetic field intensity is decreasing upward. This direction of decrease gives drifts opposite to those of Fig. 2-5, and the interface is therefore stable.

For magnetic fields of finite extent the spatial inhomogeneities shown in Fig. 2-6 must be accompanied by curvatures of the field lines as shown. That is, the field lines of a spatially decreasing field must have radii of curvature with centers situated in the regions of higher field. Thus it is apparent from Fig. 2-6 that a plasma-vacuum interface under the action of an inhomogeneous magnetic field is stable if the field lines are convex toward the plasma and unstable if they are concave toward it.

Given this criterion for the stability of a plasma, we can reconsider the pinch instability described earlier. From Fig. 2-3 it is evident that the self magnetic field of the pinch is everywhere concave toward the plasma. Thus the pinch is inherently unstable. Another manifestation of this inherent instability, besides the kink mentioned earlier, is the so-called "sausage" instability pictured in Fig. 2-7. The increased magnetic field intensity at the regions of minimum cross section causes the plasma to narrow down further at these places. The plasma at these necked regions is squeezed into the bulges, and there are no adequate restoring forces. Such discharges can actually be interrupted by being pinched apart by these sausage instabilities.

Attention has been given to inhibiting the sausage and kink instabilities by providing a "frozen-in" axial magnetic field along the pinch. This axial field tends to slow the growth of kink instabilities by requiring that they expend energy in stretching this field. Sausage instabilities also tend to be inhibited because of the compression of the axial "frozen-in" field required by their development. Nevertheless, it has not been possible in practice to prevent either form of pinch instability by use of such fields.

When the ripple instabilities are applied to a plasma located within a magnetic mirror geometry, they are often called "flute" or interchange instabilities. Figure 2-8 shows a plasma located between two magnetic mirrors. Between the mirrors near the midplane the field lines are concave toward the plasma. Hence a perturbation such as that shown in Fig. 2-8b will grow, and the interface is seen to be unstable. The fluted form of the surface gives the instability its name.

This instability can be a serious obstacle to long-term containment of plasma by mirror magnetic fields, but the situation is a bit more complicated than is evident from what has yet been said.

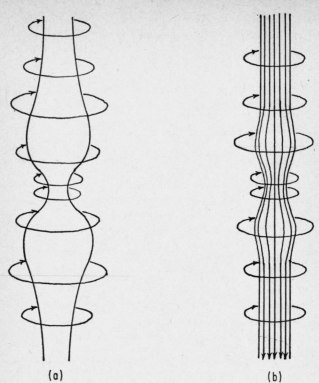

FIG. 2-7   The sausage instability of a plasma pinch (a) and the stabilizing influence of a "frozen-in" longitudinal magnetic field (b).

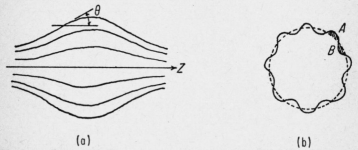

FIG. 2-8   Flute instability of a plasma in a magnetic mirror. The magnetic field configuration is shown in (a) and the flute perturbation in cross section in (b).

Although the mirror geometry is unstable at its midplane, it is not unstable near the maximum mirror fields. There the field is convex toward the plasma and is stable against "fluting." The question of over-all flute stability for the mirror configuration must include consideration of both these regions since the particles do travel throughout the entire plasma volume and are affected by conditions in both regions.

The question of over-all stability has been answered on the basis of an energy argument similar to that presented for a ball. The formation of a flute requires the interchange of plasma and magnetic field between two regions such as A and B in Fig. 2-8. To determine mirror stability, the energy required for this interchange between these regions is calculated. When this energy is greater than zero, the interchange cannot take place spontaneously and perturbations cannot grow. When the plasma pressure is small compared to the magnetic pressure, the result is that the plasma is stable if

$$\int \frac{d\theta}{B^{3/2}} > 0, \qquad (2\text{-}15)$$

where θ is the angle between the flux line and the z-axis shown in Fig. 2-8. The integral is taken from one mirror field maximum to the other.

The simplified system we have considered does not satisfy this requirement and is therefore not stable. However, there are other mitigating circumstances that may sometimes cause such mirror configurations to be stable. One omission from this discussion that does affect the stability question favorably is that of the finite size of the particle orbits with respect to that of the mirror geometry.

Obviously, if one wishes to contain a plasma against the various forms of ripple instability it is necessary to make the magnetic field everywhere convex toward the plasma. Or, put in a slightly different way, it is necessary to place the plasma in a position of minimum magnetic field. Thus any plasma perturbations will cause charge separations that oppose the perturbation. This tendency of a plasma to move toward regions of minimum magnetic field is simply a manifestation of its diamagnetic character.

Several forms of this so-called minimum-B configuration have been devised. Figure 2-9 is an example of one such arrangement which has a minimum B along the central axis. Current flows in the six conductors with adjacent currents in opposite directions. In the radial direction at any azimuth, the magnitude of the field increases away from a zero field on the axis.

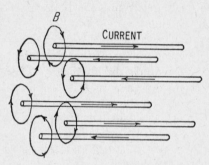

FIG. 2-9 The current in the six conductors forms a magnetic field that is zero at the center and increases with increasing radial displacements.

Of course, there is no containment of plasma along the axial direction. This lack has been countered by two different suggestions. One consists in axially extending the section shown and bending it into a torus so that there are no ends from which losses can occur. If, in addition, the conductors are twisted as they are made into a torus, the configuration used in the thermonuclear device known as the *stellarator* is produced.

The other method of controlling end losses is to superimpose upon the field shown in Fig. 2-9 a mirror field like that of Fig. 2-8. It is not immediately obvious that such a superposition will leave the field pattern of Fig. 2-9 sufficiently undisturbed that a true minimum-B configuration is attained, but this can indeed be accomplished.

In the above discussions of plasma stability we have not considered the much slower diffusion processes that also transport plasma across any magnetic fields that may be used for confinement. To obtain a comparison of the growth time for these instabilities with the diffusion times, we compare the quantity $(2\pi b/\lambda)^{-1/2}$ from Eq. 2-14 with the 10^3 sec given in Table 2-1 for diffusion of a thermonuclear plasma. Even for the relatively weak gravitational field for which $b = g = 980$ cm-sec^{-2}, if $\lambda = 1$ cm, then $(2\pi b/\lambda)^{-1/2} \approx$ 0.03 sec. For the stronger charge separation forces exerted by inhomogeneous magnetic fields, etc., the growth times may be of the order of a microsecond. Thus we see that except for stable plasma conditions on a very long time scale, diffusion processes are frequently unimportant.

§ 2-3 **Plasma Waves.** The behavior of electromagnetic waves in a plasma is generally complicated. The complications arise both because of the intricacies of electromagnetic wave phenomena themselves and because their interaction with the plasma particles can occur in such a variety of ways. To simplify the picture in any substantial way requires careful selection of the particular types of propagation to be treated and some limitation of the effects to be included in the treatment. In the following we shall make liberal use of both the selection and limiting processes in order to point out some of the essential features of plasma waves.

We begin by discussing the propagation of electromagnetic waves in free space. Such propagation is relatively straightforward and allows some discussion of waves before including the complications introduced by their interactions with a plasma. In the absence of the charged plasma particles, electromagnetic waves propagate at the velocity $c = 3 \times 10^{10}$ cm/sec. Ordinary, visible light is one manifestation of these electromagnetic waves as are radio waves, X rays, and the high-energy gamma rays. The frequency of the waves is given by $\nu = \omega/2\pi$ and is related to the wavelength λ by

$$c = \nu\lambda = \omega(\lambda/2\pi) = \omega/\kappa, \qquad (2\text{-}16)$$

where $\kappa = 2\pi/\lambda = \omega/c$ is called the *propagation constant*. (Care must be used not to confuse the Greek kappa introduced here with the k used for the Boltzmann constant.) For electromagnetic waves of a fixed frequency or wavelength it is easy to picture the wave fields that characterize the propagation. Both the electric and magnetic components of the wave are sinusoidal in both space and time. Consider a wave propagating in the z direction. At a given instant the electric and magnetic components of the wave field are as shown in Fig. 2-10. The electric field varies according to $E(z) = E_0 \sin \kappa z$, and the magnetic field varies as $B(z) = B_0 \sin \kappa z$. We

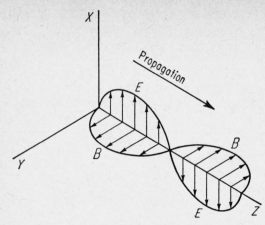

FIG. 2-10 Electric and magnetic fields associated with the propagation of a plane electromagnetic wave in the z direction in free space.

note that the $\sin \kappa z$ function passes through one complete cycle as z varies from $z = 0$ to $z = \lambda$.

At a fixed z position, $E(z)$ and $B(z)$ are both sinusoidal functions of time with $E(z,t)$ oscillating in the positive and negative x direction and $B(z,t)$ doing so in the positive and negative y direction. The combination of these space and time dependencies causes the wave shown in Fig. 2-10 to move in the z direction at the velocity c. The complete space and time dependence of E and B are given by

$$E(z,t) = E_0 \sin (\kappa z - \omega t),$$
$$B(z,t) = B_0 \sin (\kappa z - \omega t). \tag{2-17}$$

The velocity c_p of a point of constant phase in the wave is then seen to propagate according to $\kappa z - \omega t =$ a constant, from which $dz/dt = \omega/\kappa = c_p = c$. Here c_p is called the phase velocity of the wave.

Since there are no electric charges with which the electric and magnetic fields may interact, they remain mutually perpendicular to each other and to the direction of propagation. Waves for which the wave fields remain in fixed directions during propagation are said to be plane polarized. When the interaction of the electric and magnetic wave fields with the charged particles of a transmitting medium cause their directions to rotate during propagation, the plane of polarization is similarly rotated.

The characteristics of electromagnetic wave propagation in a plasma are dependent upon the effects of the charged particles and their collective behavior upon the waves. Thus a part of the present discussion reverts back to both the individual particle and the collective bases discussed in Chapter 1. It is not difficult to determine those frequency regions in which electromagnetic waves are most importantly affected by plasma interactions. Although propagation and nonpropagation of electromagnetic waves may occur over wide ranges of frequency, only near frequencies that are characteristic of the plasma or of the plasma particles will really interesting effects take place. Thus we expect large interaction effects for frequencies near the ion and electron plasma and cyclotron frequencies.

The relative influence of electric and magnetic components of the wave fields upon the plasma particles is such that the effects due to the electric components far exceed those due to the magnetic components when the particle velocities are small compared to that of light. Thus in the discussion that follows we neglect the effects of the wave magnetic fields. Another simplification which is useful in a variety of physical situations also serves to keep the following discussion from becoming too complicated. This simplification consists of neglecting all collision effects between the plasma particles.

Proceeding on this basis, we consider the propagation of electromagnetic waves through a transmitting medium. For the transmission of light in a dielectric medium, a *dielectric constant* K is defined: $K \equiv c^2/c_p^2$. In free space (a vacuum) $K = 1$, since $c_p = c$ as noted above. In a transmitting material such as glass, $c_p < c$ and the dielectric constant $K > 1$. This same dielectric constant also relates the displacement current j_D that flows through a dielectric as a result of the time rate of charge of an electric field applied to the dielectric. The relation is

$$dE/dt = 4\pi j_D/K. \qquad (2\text{-}18)$$

For an applied electric field $E = E_0 \sin \omega t$, the displacement current, from Eq. 2-18, is $j_D = (KE_0/4\pi)\omega \cos \omega t$.

If the medium to which this electric field is applied not only has dielectric properties described by K but also contains mobile charged particles, the total current will be the sum of that due to the displacement current and that due to the charged particles. In a plasma the electrons are the most mobile of the particles present, and they contribute by far the largest portion of the charged particle current. To determine the electron contribution to the total current, the equation of motion of electrons subject to the field E is written

$$m(dv/dt) = eE = eE_0 \sin \omega t, \qquad (2\text{-}19)$$

where m, v, and e are the electron mass, velocity, and charge, respectively. From Eq. 2-19 the electron velocity is $v = -(E_0 e/\omega m) \cos \omega t$. This velocity produces an electron current $nev = -(E_0 n e^2/m\omega) \cos \omega t$ which, together with the displacement current deduced from Eq. 2-18, yields a total current

$$j = \left(K - \frac{4\pi n e^2}{m\omega^2} \right) \frac{\omega E_0}{4\pi} \cos \omega t. \qquad (2\text{-}20)$$

The effect of the electrons upon the total current produced by the electric field E is to reduce the effective dielectric constant by $4\pi n e^2/m\omega^2 = \omega_p^2/\omega^2$ from the value K. Here $\omega_p = 2\pi\nu_p$, and ν_p is the plasma frequency given by Eq. 1-11. For electrons in a vacuum, $K = 1$, and the effective dielectric constant is given by

$$K' = c^2/c_p{}^2 = \frac{c^2 \kappa^2}{\omega^2} = 1 - \left(\frac{\omega_p}{\omega} \right)^2,$$

which can be rewritten

$$\kappa^2 = (\omega^2 - \omega_p{}^2)/c^2. \qquad (2\text{-}21)$$

The electric field $E = E_0 \sin \omega t$ represents the primary influence of an electromagnetic wave, and Eq. 2-21 directly relates the propagation constant and the wave frequency of such waves. If the effects of the plasma ions are added to those of the electrons, Eq. 2-21 is very slightly modified by an ion plasma frequency term that does not appreciably affect the result as stated. Equations such as Eq. 2-21 that relate the propagation constant κ to the wave frequency ω are often called *dispersion relations*. From Eq. 2-21 we see that when $\omega > \omega_p$, the propagation constant is real, and the electromagnetic wave will propagate without attenuation. When $\omega < \omega_p$, the propagation constant is imaginary and this indicates a rapid wave attenuation. Thus the plasma electrons are capable of rapidly reducing the effective wave field when the wave frequency is lower than the plasma frequency.

We can see the physical role played by the plasma frequency in determining the frequency at which the electrons can inhibit propagation. First, note that the plasma frequency ω_p can be related to the Debye length $D = (kT/4\pi ne^2)^{1/2}$. That is,

$$\omega_p \equiv (4\pi ne^2/m)^{1/2} = (kT/m)^{1/2}/D. \tag{2-22}$$

Now $(kT/m)^{1/2}$ is approximately the mean electron velocity. Thus $1/\omega_p$ is approximately the mean time required for an electron to move a distance equal to a Debye length. As shown in § 1-1, the Debye length is the distance over which a plasma can maintain an appreciable charge separation or electric field. Thus as the wave frequency increases above ω_p, the electron velocities are inadequate to maintain the electric fields in the plasma interior near their quiescent values. For wave frequencies below ω_p the electron velocities are adequate to this role and incident electromagnetic waves are screened out.

It is interesting to note how the *phase* and *group velocities* determined from Eq. 2-21, namely:

$$\begin{aligned} c_p &\equiv \omega/\kappa = c/[1 - (\omega_p/\omega)^2]^{1/2}, \\ c_g &\equiv d\omega/d\kappa = c[1 - (\omega_p/\omega)^2]^{1/2}, \end{aligned} \tag{2-23}$$

vary with frequency for a collisionless plasma. At all frequencies the phase velocity exceeds that of light in a vacuum and approaches infinity as the wave frequency approaches ω_p. The group velocity is always less than c and goes to zero and becomes imaginary as the frequency drops below ω_p. The latter is another indication of the attenuation of waves at less than the plasma frequency. A direct and simple criterion that determines such a "cutoff" frequency is that $\kappa = 0$. In Eq. 2-23 the fact that $c_p c_g = c^2$ is entirely accidental. The attenuation below cutoff occurs at a rate such that the field intensity is reduced to $1/e$ of its value on penetration of a "skin depth" of thickness

$$d = \frac{c}{\omega_p}\left(1 - \frac{\omega^2}{\omega_p{}^2}\right)^{-1/2}. \tag{2-24}$$

When the plasma is immersed in a uniform, static magnetic field, the behavior of propagated waves can be considerably more complicated than in the preceding discussion. The critical factor in simplifying the discussion is the direction of wave propagation with respect to the magnetic field. Two cases will be discussed: propagation perpendicular to the field B with the wave electric field parallel to B, and propagation parallel to B. In both instances only the limiting, collisionless cases will be considered.

Propagation perpendicular to B with the E wave field parallel to B can be visualized from Fig. 2-10 if B is taken in the x direction. Consideration of the individual charged particles indicates that motions due to the wave electric field will be parallel to B and hence unaffected by it. Since the corresponding particle motions due to the wave magnetic field are negligible compared to those due to the electric field, the over-all effect of B upon the particles and the waves is negligible. Thus the dispersion relations and other results discussed above are equally applicable to this case.

If the wave electric field is not parallel to B, the charged-particle motion and its effect upon the wave is more complicated and the results are not the same as those for $B = 0$. For waves propagating parallel to B, the wave E field is perpendicular to B as shown in Fig. 2-11. Of course, thermal motions of the ions and electrons cause

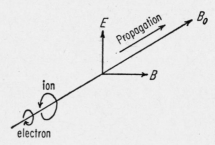

FIG. 2-11   **Propagation of an electromagnetic wave in the direction of the magnetic field in which a plasma is immersed.**

them to gyrate about the magnetic field at their respective cyclotron frequencies, $\omega_{ci} = ZeB/M$ and $\omega_{ce} = -eB/m$, given by Eq. 1-17. If the wave electric field were in a direction such that it could couple to this gyration, resonances would be expected when the wave frequency equals either cyclotron frequency.

Propagation at all frequencies is affected by the gyrating charged particles. The most straightforward way to see how the particle-wave interaction takes place is to consider a circularly polarized electromagnetic wave instead of the plane polarized one discussed above. In a circularly polarized wave the electric field rotates about the propagation direction once each period as the wave proceeds through the medium. Thus a wave electric field can rotate in synchronism with a gyrating particle if the wave frequency equals the particle cyclotron frequency. Such a synchronous rotation of wave electric field and particle will cause a strong interaction and hence an efficient energy interchange between the two. Since ions and electrons gyrate in opposite senses about the magnetic field lines, it is useful to discuss the propagation in terms of right- and left-hand circularly polarized waves so that interactions with both particle species may be efficiently treated.

Fortunately, it is possible to decompose the linearly polarized wave field that we originally discussed into its two oppositely circularly polarized components. How these two circularly polarized components add to form the linearly polarized wave field is shown in Fig. 2-12. From Fig. 2-11 it is evident that the right-hand cir-

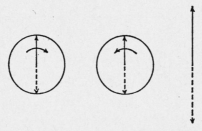

FIG. 2-12 The addition of two circularly polarized vectors to yield a harmonically oscillating plane-polarized vector. Only the vertical components do not cancel in the additions.

cularly polarized component rotates in the same direction as the electrons, while the left-hand component rotates in the direction of the ions. Since each component rotates in the same sense as one type of particle, that component is more strongly coupled to the motions of those particles. This preferential coupling to particles of differing mass causes the two components to have different propagation constants. And, of course, each of the propagation constants corresponds to a different wave velocity.

Special cases of these two circularly polarized waves occur at the cyclotron frequencies of each type of particle. At a wave frequency equal to the electron cyclotron frequency the right-hand wave is in resonance with the electrons. That is, the electric field will rotate in synchronism with the gyrating electrons. The electrons can then acquire energy from the synchronized electric field. At a wave frequency equal to the ion cyclotron frequency the left-hand polarized wave is in resonance with the ions. In this case the ions may extract energy from the wave as they gyrate in synchronism with the wave electric field.

The two different propagation constants associated with the right and left circularly-polarized waves are given by an analysis of the same type used to deduce Eq. 2-21. When the currents carried by the ions as well as the electrons and the effects of the magnetic field upon the equations of particle motion are included, the resulting dispersion relations are

$$\kappa_r{}^2 = \frac{\omega^2}{c^2}\left(1 - \frac{\omega_{pe}{}^2}{\omega^2 + \omega\omega_{ce}} - \frac{\omega_{pi}{}^2}{\omega^2 + \omega\omega_{ci}}\right) \qquad (2\text{-}25)$$

and

$$\kappa_l{}^2 = \frac{\omega^2}{c^2}\left(1 - \frac{\omega_{pe}{}^2}{\omega^2 - \omega\omega_{ce}} - \frac{\omega_{pi}{}^2}{\omega^2 - \omega\omega_{ci}}\right), \qquad (2\text{-}26)$$

where ω_{pe} and ω_{pi} are the electron and ion plasma frequencies, respectively. Note that κ_r goes to infinity, indicating a resonance, when $\omega = |eB/m|$, and κ_l goes to infinity when $\omega = ZeB/M$. In checking for these resonances it is important to bear in mind the signs carried by the defining equations for the two cyclotron frequencies. That is, ω_{ce} is negative and ω_{ci} is positive. Since $|\omega_{pe}| \gg |\omega_{pi}|$ because of the differing masses of electrons and ions, the last term in Eq. 2-25 can usually be neglected and the effects upon this wave component are determined very largely by the electrons. Near ion cyclotron resonance the last term in Eq. 2-26 often is much larger than the second, and the effects near this resonance are largely due to the ions. Further, both κ_r and κ_l reduce to the simple dispersion relation given by Eq. 2-21 when $\omega_{ce} = \omega_{ci} = 0$ and $\omega_{pi} \ll \omega_{pe}$.

The complications introduced into the dispersion relations by the addition of a magnetic field also change the conditions for which propagation can occur without large attenuation. Such attenuation occurs when the group velocity goes to zero, or when the phase velocity goes to infinity, which is equivalent to the propagation constant going to zero. Considering only the effect of the electrons upon the right-hand wave, $\kappa_r = 0$ or imaginary for $\omega_{pe}^2 \geqslant \omega^2 + \omega\omega_{ce}$. This result is a modification of the corresponding requirement for cut-off in the absence of B_0, which was that $\omega^2 \leqslant \omega_{pe}^2$.

For waves of sufficiently low frequency all of the effects due to cyclotron resonances and plasma oscillations can be neglected. The plasma behaves like an unconstrained conducting fluid and can thus be discussed from a macroscopic viewpoint. Waves at these frequencies are called *hydromagnetic waves*. Such waves provide a clear example of the manner in which the electromagnetic waves propagated by a plasma are inextricably meshed with the motions of the plasma particles and hence with the macroscopic behavior of the plasma.

Suppose that a plane electromagnetic wave with the frequency limits $\omega \ll \omega_{ce}$, $\omega \ll \omega_{ci}$, $\omega \ll \omega_p$ is propagated in a plasma along the direction of a uniform, static magnetic field. The wave magnetic field is transverse and hence perpendicular to the static field. The effect of the wave on the static field is to produce "ripples" along it, as shown in Fig. 2-13. If there were no plasma, these ripples (which constitute the wave magnetic field) would propagate at the speed of light. However, in a plasma the situation is different.

For wave periods that are short compared to the diffusion times

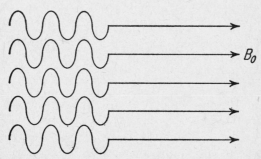

FIG. 2-13 Superposition of a wave magnetic field upon a static field B_0.

the magnetic fields of the wave are frozen into the fluid. They thereby force the fluid to move along the flux lines. Since the fluid is thus tied to the wave fields, the wave velocity is slowed by the inertial effects of the fluid. This situation is analogous to the propagation of waves along a string where the wave velocity is given in terms of the tension T and the linear mass density ρ of the string as

$$v = (T/\rho)^{1/2}. \qquad (2\text{-}27)$$

Making the analogy to hydromagnetic plasma waves, we replace the string tension T by the magnetic tension along the field lines, $B^2/4\pi$, indicated in Fig. 2-2, and ρ becomes the plasma mass density. Thus for these hydromagnetic waves we might expect the velocity to be

$$V_A = (B^2/4\pi\rho)^{1/2}. \qquad (2\text{-}28)$$

This velocity V_A is often called the *Alfvén velocity* after Hannes Alfvén, who first recognized that such hydromagnetic waves are possible.

Hydromagnetic waves are simply the low frequency limit of the electromagnetic waves treated above. For propagation along the static magnetic field the various properties of these waves can be obtained from that treatment. In particular, the Alfvén velocity for hydromagnetic waves may be obtained in a direct (and more satisfying) manner from the propagation constants given in Eqs. 2-25 and 2-26. On substituting the values for the plasma and cyclotron frequencies, then making the approximation that the wave frequency is small compared to either of the plasma or cyclotron frequencies, we can write the phase velocity $c_p = \omega/\kappa$ as

$$c_p = c \Big/ \left(1 + \frac{4\pi n_e M c^2}{B^2}\right)^{1/2}. \qquad (2\text{-}29)$$

Since $n_e = n_i$, $n_e M$ can be written as ρ, the plasma mass density. Under almost all plasma conditions the second term in the square root is large compared to unity, hence Eq. 2-29 is accurately approximated by

$$c_p = (B^2/4\pi\rho)^{1/2}. \qquad (2\text{-}30)$$

This phase velocity is just the Alfvén velocity given by Eq. 2-28.

Since the Alfvén velocity is generally the fastest speed at which electromagnetic changes may be transmitted in a plasma, it is useful to have an estimate of its magnitude under certain typical conditions. In a laboratory plasma in which $B = 10,000$ gauss and

$\rho = 10^{-8}$ gm/cm^3, corresponding to hydrogen gas at about 100 microns pressure, $V_A \approx 3 \times 10^7$ cm/sec. In the solar corona, where the field may be in the neighborhood of 10^{-2} gauss and $\rho = 10^{-16}$ gm/cm^3, the velocity is $V_A \approx 3 \times 10^5$ cm/sec. In the galactic arms the magnetic field may be 10^{-5} gauss and the density may be in the neighborhood of 10^{-24} gm/cm^3; these values yield an Alfvén velocity of about 3×10^6 cm/sec.

The velocity given by Eq. 2-30 is accurate for Alfvén waves only when the approximations concerning the wave frequency are met and when the magnetic field amplitudes associated with the wave are small compared with the steady field along which they propagate. If the small-amplitude condition is not met, the total magnetic pressure in the plasma is not approximately constant, but depends upon the time-dependent wave field. The phase velocity is changed from that given by Eq. 2-30 by adding a term representing the effect of the time-dependent wave magnetic field $b(t)$ upon the pressure. The phase velocity then becomes

$$c_p^2 = [B^2 + b(t)^2]/4\pi\rho. \qquad (2\text{-}31)$$

This equation indicates that the larger portions of the wave field will travel at higher speed than the lower portions. The result is to cause the leading portions of the waves to be steepened as the larger amplitudes overtake the smaller. The steepening will develop into what is called a hydromagnetic shock wave in which the initial rise of the wave magnetic field, in the absence of dissipative mechanisms, is infinitely fast. In actual fact, of course, dissipative mechanisms will limit the maximum steepness that the leading portion of the shock wave may attain. In § 3-3, experimental observations of the steepening of large-amplitude hydromagnetic waves are discussed.

Various laboratory experiments have been performed that indicate the general validity of the dispersion relations given here for the propagation of electromagnetic waves by plasma. Indeed, many of the effects are so well documented that they may be used to measure various of the plasma properties on which the predicted behavior depends. For example, a measurement of the plasma frequency can be used to infer the electron density in the plasma. These and other laboratory plasma experiments are described in Chapter 3.

3   *Laboratory Plasmas*

For more than 100 years gaseous discharges have been the subject of laboratory experiments. The earliest experiments appear to have been done by Plücker in 1850. In 1859 he showed that in an electrical discharge between electrodes in a rarefied gas some sort of "rays" proceeding from the discharge cathode can be deflected by a magnetic field. Demonstrating these "cathode rays" before the British Association in London in 1879, Crookes prophesied that they would be the means of solving the biggest problems in physics. His accuracy became evident as the work of J. J. Thomson and others revealed the detailed properties of the rays in terms of the particles we now call electrons.

Various types of discharges and plasmas are discussed in this chapter. Whereas the earlier chapters have dealt with certain of the more theoretical aspects, we now proceed to a more phenomenological description of plasma as it exists in laboratory experiments. We first discuss the formation of a plasma by the ionization or breakdown of a neutral gas by application of various electric and magnetic fields. The degree to which the plasma is ionized depends upon the quantity of energy dissipated in the plasma by these fields. With comparatively little energy a slightly ionized, self-sustaining plasma may be formed by a glow discharge. Dissipation of larger amounts of energy can lead to highly ionized plasmas that are generally of a transient character. Numerous techniques are available for analyzing the properties of such plasmas. Some of these techniques use the light emitted from the plasma, some use plasma-particle sampling procedures, and some take advantage of the various interactions that electromagnetic fields have with plasma.

Very many plasma experiments have been performed to test

and help expand plasma theory. A recent use of plasma spectroscopic experiments is to explore the highly excited atomic states that may be of astrophysical interest. Most of the experiments we consider in this chapter are of recent vintage and are included to illustrate some aspects of current laboratory plasma research.

In the first parts of the discussion the term "gaseous discharge" or simply "discharge" will be frequently encountered. These terms designate the conduction of electrical current by an ionized gas whether or not a plasma, as defined in Chapter 1, exists.

§ 3-1 Ionization and Breakdown. A quick calculation serves to illustrate that the ionization of a gas is ordinarily not as simple as just pulling electrons from ions by means of an applied electric field. In hydrogen the electron and ion have charges $|e| = 4.8 \times 10^{-10}$ esu and are separated by a distance $r = 5 \times 10^{-9}$ cm. The force of attraction between the two charges is e^2/r^2, and the electric field required to separate them is e/r^2. This field turns out to be of the order of 5×10^9 volts/cm; it is readily apparent that very much smaller fields are quite adequate to produce ionization and hence electrical conduction in a gas. Thus other processes than direct, electric field ionization are evidently important.

As a general organizational pattern for discussing the various types of gaseous discharge, we begin with those involving the lowest conduction currents and progress to the highest. For the discussion in this section we consider the gas to be contained in an insulating tube such as that shown in Fig. 3-1. Into each end of the tube is

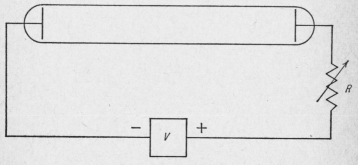

FIG. 3-1 A discharge tube.

inserted an electrode. Between these electrodes is connected a power supply in series with a suitable resistance for controlling the discharge current. The gas pressure and composition may be varied.

Below about 10^{-11} amperes or so, the amount of ionization required for such a current to flow is not sustained by the current flow itself. Additional energy must be supplied to the gas to prevent the current from dying out. Such discharges are called nonself-sustaining.

The external energy required for such discharges may be supplied in a variety of ways. A direct means is to add the requisite ionization energy to the gas atoms by radiation of an appropriate wavelength λ. If the ionization energy is eV_i, radiation of frequency

$$\nu = c/\lambda = eV_i/h \qquad (3\text{-}1)$$

or larger will produce ionization when absorbed by the atom. Here $h = 6.62 \times 10^{-27}$ erg sec is Planck's constant. Using the appropriate conversion factors, Eq. 3-1 becomes

$$eV_i\lambda = 12\ 398, \qquad (3\text{-}2)$$

where eV_i is in electron volts (eV) and λ is in Ångstrom units (Å). Thus to ionize an atom with $eV_i = 10$ eV, radiation of wavelength $\lambda = 1239.8$ Å or less is required. This wavelength is in the ultraviolet. Since ionization energies are of this order (see Table 1-1), ultraviolet radiation can be expected to be of importance in gas discharges.

Of course, the ionization necessary to sustain the discharge could be achieved by heating the gas by external means. If one interprets "external means" to include chemical combination, a flame is a nonself-sustaining ionized gas. Here the ionization is maintained by the heat added to the gas by chemical reaction of the fuel with oxygen.

In addition to conduction by the ions and electrons of the gas, current can be carried by the addition of charged particles to the gas. For example, a heated cathode can furnish electrons that permeate the gas and render it conducting. If the voltage across the tube is sufficiently high, the electrons emitted by the cathode can acquire sufficient energy to produce further ionization of the gas by collisions.

Once there are ions and electrons in the gas, the situation becomes quite complicated. Under the action of the applied electric field the ions and electrons move in opposite directions through the gas. However, in doing so they suffer collisions with other ions, electrons, and gas atoms. These collisions are of great importance to the discharge. To evaluate the relative roles played by the ions and electrons, their relative velocities will be compared. This is easily done by noting their speeds after they pass through a given potential difference V where the increase of kinetic energy equals the decrease in potential energy. Thus for electrons and ions starting from rest

$$\begin{aligned} \tfrac{1}{2}mv_e{}^2 &= |eV|, \\ \tfrac{1}{2}Mv_i{}^2 &= |eV|, \end{aligned} \tag{3-3}$$

where m and M are electron and ion masses, respectively. For $V = 10$ volts the electron velocity is $v_e = 1.8 \times 10^8$ cm/sec, and for the hydrogen ion $v_i = 4.5 \times 10^6$ cm/sec. For equal ion and electron densities it is evident that most of the discharge current $i = n_i e v_i - n_e e v_e$ is carried by the electrons due to their high relative velocity.

Both the ions and electrons suffer two different types of collisions, elastic and inelastic. These differ in that the kinetic energy of the colliding particles is conserved in an elastic but not in an inelastic collision. In inelastic collisions the change in kinetic energy is compensated by a change in the internal energy of one or both of the colliding particles.

The dynamics of elastic collisions involves the conservation of kinetic energy and momentum of the particles. From these conservation requirements it turns out that electrons can transfer only a small amount of their kinetic energy to ions by elastic collision and that ions can transfer nearly all of their kinetic energy to neutral gas atoms. To see this result we consider a head-on collision. For particles of mass m_1 and m_2 and with m_2 initially at rest, conservation of momentum p requires that

$$p_{1b} = p_{1a} + p_{2a}, \tag{3-4}$$

where the subscripts b and a refer to values before and after collision. The kinetic energy is $E = \tfrac{1}{2}mv^2 = p^2/2m$. Thus its conservation requires

$$\frac{p_{1b}{}^2}{2m_1} = \frac{p_{1a}{}^2}{2m_1} + \frac{p_{2a}{}^2}{2m_2}. \tag{3-5}$$

Eq. 3-4 can be written as

$$p_{1b}^2 + p_{1a}^2 - 2p_{1b}p_{1a} = p_{2a}^2, \qquad (3\text{-}6)$$

and Eq. 3-5 as

$$\frac{p_{1b}^2 - p_{1a}^2}{m_1} = \frac{p_{2a}^2}{m_2}. \qquad (3\text{-}7)$$

Combining Eqs. 3-6 and 3-7 yields

$$\frac{p_{2a}}{p_{1b}} = \frac{2m_2}{m_1 + m_2}. \qquad (3\text{-}8)$$

For $m_1 = m_2$, $p_{2a} = p_{1a}$; hence in such a collision particle 2 assumes the total kinetic energy of particle 1. This is the case for ion-atom collisions. If $m_2 \gg m_1$, the ratio of kinetic energies becomes

$$\frac{E_{2a}}{E_{1b}} = \left(\frac{p_{2a}}{p_{1b}}\right)^2 \frac{m_1}{m_2} \approx \frac{4m_1}{m_2}, \qquad (3\text{-}9)$$

using Eq. 3-8 for the ratio (p_{2a}/p_{1b}). For $m_1/m_2 \approx 1/1800$ as for electrons colliding with hydrogen ions, only 4/1800 of the electron energy is transferred to the ion.

Thus we see that the ions, because of their greater mass, do not acquire much velocity either from the applied field or from the electrons. What energy they have is easily transferred to the neutral gas atoms. The electrons, on the other hand, acquire and maintain their velocities easily and can thus contribute to further ionization and excitation by inelastic collision processes.

Two important inelastic collision processes suffered by electrons are the excitation and ionization of atoms. As already mentioned in § 1-4, ionization involves the removal of electrons from atoms with energy requirements such as those listed in Table 1-1; excitation raises the atomic energy level above the ground state, but does not ionize. Thus considerably less than 10 eV are ordinarily required for excitation. Most atomic states, when so excited, decay in times of the order of 10^{-8} sec with the emission of radiation characteristic of the state energy. Certain states have longer lifetimes, for example, 0.1 sec or more. These states are called *metastable*. They can have important consequences for the ionization of mixtures of gases. When the ionization energy of one component of the mixture is less than the energy of the metastable state, atoms of this component may be ionized by absorption of the excitation energy during collision with the metastable atoms.

Aside from excitation and ionization, electrons can lose energy only slowly by elastic collisions. Of course, after the electrons arrive at the anode of the discharge tube they heat it with their remaining kinetic energy.

The relative importance of the various energy-loss mechanisms for electrons is dependent upon the energy-dependent cross sections for each. Thus the effectiveness of each mechanism depends upon the energy acquired by the electrons from the applied field between successive collisions. This energy is simply the electric field E multiplied by the mean scattering length between collisions. Since the mean scattering length is inversely proportional to the gas pressure p_0, the effective energy is proportional to E/p_0 and the various electron mechanisms are usually discussed in terms of this parameter.

If the voltage drop across the discharge tube is sufficiently great, the discharge becomes self-sustaining. The transition between the nonself-sustaining and the self-sustaining discharge is shown in Fig. 3-2 to occur for currents of the order of 10^{-11} amperes. The term *Townsend discharge*, after the physicist who studied this phenomenon, is often applied to a discharge operating between points B and C of Fig. 3-2. At the transition voltage, the combined discharge processes that create the ionization are adequate to its maintenance. However, a discharge tube with an applied voltage adequate to produce a self-sustaining discharge will not spontaneously "break down" (that is, conduct a current of 10^{-7} to 10^{-6} amperes) unless an outside influence causes some ionization. Ordinarily, cosmic rays are the outside influence that intervenes to produce the initiating ionization.

Once ionization is caused by such an influence, the electron can gain sufficient energy between collisions to produce additional ionization. These additional free electrons are also subject to the applied field and can likewise further increase the ionization. The result is a rapid build-up of the ionization level and of the conducted current.

The self-sustaining discharge requirement may be put in the following mathematical form. In general, the number dn of new

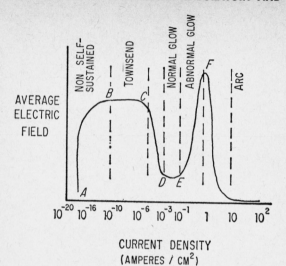

FIG. 3-2 Average electric field as a function of current density for a gaseous discharge.

electrons per unit volume produced in a distance dx along an applied electric field E is proportional to E and to the electron density n. That is,

$$dn = \epsilon E n \, dx, \qquad (3\text{-}10)$$

where ϵ is the number of new electrons per volt per original electron. Eq. 3-10 can be integrated to yield

$$n = n_0 \exp (\epsilon E x). \qquad (3\text{-}11)$$

If $x = d$, the distance between the electrodes, then $Ed = V_B$ and is called the breakdown voltage, which is characterized by the onset of the self-sustained discharge. Thus

$$n = n_0 \exp (\epsilon V_B). \qquad (3\text{-}12)$$

In addition to this multiplying process within the gas, the positive ions that migrate toward the cathode under the influence of the applied field cause secondary electron emission from the cathode. If each ion produces χ secondary electrons, the total number of electrons produced by the two processes is $\chi(n - n_0)$. In order for the discharge to be self-sustaining in the absence of electron loss processes this number must be equal to n_0. Thus from Eq. 3-12

$$\chi[\exp{(\epsilon V_B)} - 1] = 1. \qquad (3\text{-}13)$$

Ordinarily $\exp{(\epsilon V_B)} \gg 1$ and the one is dropped from this expression. ϵ and χ are called the first and second Townsend coefficients. ϵ is dependent upon the characteristics of the gas and χ upon those of the gas and the cathode material.

Figure 3-3 shows a plot of ϵ as a function of E/p_0 for air, argon, and neon. The maxima occur because at low pressures there are few atoms present to produce ionization and at high pressures the

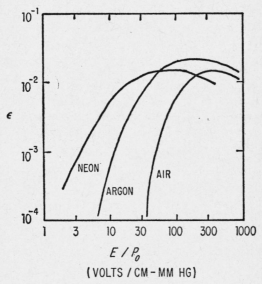

FIG. 3-3   First Townsend coefficient ϵ as a function of E/p_0 for air, argon, and neon. (Reprinted from Penning, *Electrical Discharge in Gases*, by permission of the publisher)

density is so great that the energy gain between collisions is inadequate to produce ionization.

In the Townsend discharge described above there is no appreciable space charge between anode and cathode, and the electric field is more or less uniform across the tube. However, if the discharge current is allowed to increase by decreasing the series resistance, ions begin to collect in the neighborhood of the cathode.

This positive space charge tends to concentrate the applied field over a shorter distance. In the absence of the current limiting resistor, it would cause an escalating increase in current and ionization. When the current is allowed to increase to a few milliamperes, the total voltage across the tube reaches a minimum. This low voltage region between D and E of the characteristic curve of Fig. 3-2 represents the *glow discharge*.

The physical appearance and properties of the glow discharge are markedly different from those of the Townsend discharge. Figure 3-4 shows a sketch of a discharge tube operating in this mode together with plots of potential and net space charge distributions. This discharge is virtually wholly maintained by the secondary electrons produced by positive ion bombardment of the

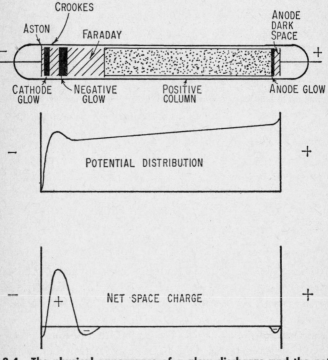

FIG. 3-4 The physical appearance of a glow discharge and the potential and net space charge distribution within it.

cathode. The various regions of luminous and dark spaces in the glow discharge are reasonably well understood; the following is a very brief account of them.

Secondary electrons produced by ion bombardment accumulate in the Aston dark space, and some of them recombine with incoming positive ions to form the cathode glow at the outer edge of this dark space. Other electrons from the Aston dark space move through the cathode glow without being captured and are accelerated in the Crookes dark space by the positive ion space charge. Sufficient energy is gained in the Crookes dark space to cause inelastic collisions and excitation of the gas to produce the negative glow. The anode edge of the negative glow signals the point at which the electron energy is too low to produce further excitation. The electrons are further accelerated in the Faraday dark space and produce the positive column that extends almost to the anode. In the positive column the net space charge is zero. The positive column is a plasma.

The number of electrons in the positive-column plasma is controlled by an additional factor beyond those described above, namely, loss to the walls of the tube. Since the current is constant along the positive column and is carried largely by the electrons, the loss of electrons to the walls must be balanced by corresponding gains from ionization within the column. The production of electrons throughout the interior of the column and their higher diffusion rate cause a radial distribution of the electron density that is highest at the tube axis and lowest at the walls. This electron density distribution produces a radial electric field that influences the radial movement of the electrons and ions. The electron diffusion rate is slowed and the ion rate is increased by this electric field. If the mean scattering length is small compared to the tube radius, an *ambipolar diffusion* coefficient can be defined. This coefficient describes the rate at which ions and electrons may diffuse while satisfying the quasineutrality condition $n_e \approx n_i$. The result is that the ions and electrons diffuse together at a rate which is twice that for the free diffusion of ions. The radial distribution of ions and electrons is given in terms of the ambipolar diffusion coefficient D_a as

$$n = n(0) J_0 (r\sqrt{\nu_i/D_a}), \qquad (3\text{-}14)$$

where $n(0)$ is the electron density at $r = 0$ and J_0 is a Bessel function, which for small values of $R(\nu_i/D_a)^{1/2}$ has a nearly parabolic dependence on r. That is, $J_0(r) \approx 1 - (r/2)^2$. ν_i is the electron ionization frequency.

If the recombination rate at the walls is high, the electron density at that radius $r = R$ is essentially zero. This requires that the first zero of the Bessel function J_0 occur at $r = R$. That is, $J_0[R(\nu_i/D_a)^{1/2}] = 0$, which has the solution $R(\nu_i/D_a)^{1/2} = 2.40$, or

$$\frac{1}{\nu_i} = \frac{R^2}{(2.40)^2 D_a}. \tag{3-15}$$

The term $1/\nu_i$ is the average time between ionizations. This time must equal the average time required for an electron to migrate to the wall, and this is what the right-hand side of Eq. 3-15 represents.

If a magnetic field acts parallel to the axis of the positive column, the effective diffusion coefficient is reduced to $D_b = D_a/(1 + \omega_{ce}^2/\nu_c^2)$. Here $\omega_{ce} = Be/m$, and ν_c is the electron collision frequency. Thus it is evident that as the magnetic field is increased, the rate of electron diffusion is decreased and the condition given by Eq. 3-15 is relaxed. One might suspect that in a longitudinal magnetic field the ions, being more massive, will be less constrained than electrons from radial diffusion. However, the electric field created by radial distribution of the electrons still tends to restrain the ions. Thus the ions as well should diffuse at approximately the electron rate. This situation holds at low fields except under circumstances where conducting surfaces (for example, electrodes) are located perpendicular to the magnetic field at the ends of the discharge. In this case, the ion diffusion may be greatly enhanced over ambipolar diffusion. The ions and electrons can easily stream along the field lines to the conducting surfaces. If the plasma makes good electrical contact with these surfaces, they can provide a short-circuiting effect upon the radial field distribution, thereby allowing a much higher ion diffusion rate.

As the current of the normal glow discharge is increased, the current density at the cathode does not change. Instead, more and more of the cathode area is involved in the discharge. However, after the entire cathode is participating in the discharge, additional current can be drawn only if accompanied by a corresponding increase in the voltage. This so-called *abnormal glow discharge* is shown between E and F in Fig. 3-2. As the current density increases, so also does the positive space charge and the field at the cathode. Finally, the energy deposited at the cathode by the positive ions is great enough that thermal emission of electrons begins to occur. Then the voltage across the discharge can drop to the very low value characteristic of an *arc discharge*.

A gaseous discharge can also be formed by the application of alternating fields to the gas. These fields may be applied as shown in Fig. 3-1, inductively by a coil wrapped around the discharge tube, or by placing the gas in a waveguide. Ordinarily, the frequency of the applied field is of the order of megacycles per second or higher. In order for such a discharge to be self-sustained, the average input power going into ionization must be adequate to take care of the diffusion losses of the electrons.

§ 3-2 **High Temperature Plasmas.** For a plasma in local thermodynamic equilibrium the level of ionization and the electron temperature are closely linked. The relation between them is given by the Saha equation, Eq. 1-40. As the electron temperature is raised, the population of the higher energy states, including those of ionization, are increased at the expense of the lower states. Thus the electron temperature and the level of ionization of a plasma are raised together by imparting more energy to the electrons.

In general, the electrons absorb energy much more readily from applied electric fields than do the ions. This effect is easily seen from the fact that the *rate* of energy absorption is proportional to particle velocity, and as we noted before, the electron velocities far exceed those of the ions. Exceptions to the general rule occur when the frequency of the applied fields coincide with certain ion frequencies such as that due to cyclotron motion or when gross plasma motions are induced by appropriate combinations of electric and magnetic fields. Except for such situations, the electrons are primarily affected as electrical energies are dissipated in a plasma. Their energy increases by the same Joule heating mechanisms that operate in the electric-current heating of any medium.

The plasma ions absorb energy only slowly from the electrons. In the last section we saw that only about 4/1800 of an electron's energy is transferred to a hydrogen ion at each collision. Thus for energies much in excess of that required for complete ionization, the electrons tend not to be in thermal equilibrium with the ions. For such energies, only when the ions are directly heated or where the plasma is suitably contained for the requisite equilibrating times are the electron and ion temperatures equal. To produce a high temperature plasma therefore requires heating mechanisms that can supply energy to the electrons and ions at a rate that exceeds that lost by radiation and particles.

An example of a not particularly hot plasma will be given to illustrate the amounts of energy required for plasma heating. Consider a hydrogen plasma of approximately 5×10^{15} cm^{-3} particle density. To ionize and heat such a plasma to an ion and electron temperature of 2–4 eV requires about 10 joules per liter of plasma. If there are no instability mechanisms whereby the plasma is lost to containing walls, then the recombination rate sets a decay time of the order of 100 μsec for this plasma. To achieve the 2–4 eV temperatures requires the 10 joules to be dissipated in a time that is small compared to 100 μsec, say, 10 μsec. The power level is then (10 joules/10 $\times$ 10^{-6} sec) = 10^6 watts per liter. For a discharge voltage of 1000 volts, 1000 amperes are required.

The power requirements, even for this relatively modest plasma temperature, are sufficiently great that such discharges are ordinarily operated on a pulsed, not a continuous, basis. Therefore, experiments using plasmas having such energy requirements must also ordinarily be performed on a transient basis. For plasma of even higher energy content this limitation becomes even more difficult to avoid.

Several methods have been developed that show some promise of providing plasmas with temperatures, electron and ion, exceeding a few tens of electron volts. The heating methods that are described here are ohmic, magnetic compression, and ion cyclotron resonance heating.

The passage of current through a plasma heats the electrons directly by allowing them to extract energy from the applied electric fields. Addition of energy by this process is called *ohmic* or *Joule heating*. An example of ohmic heating occurs in the pinch discharge discussed in § 2-1. The high currents passed by the pinch not only produce the magnetic pinching, but also contribute much heating of the plasma electrons.

As already mentioned, the ions are only indirectly heated by these currents. However, the ions do affect the manner in which the electrons absorb energy. When the energy absorbed by the electrons between collisions with ions is small compared to their kinetic energy, the collisions tend to maintain the electrons in a Boltzmann energy distribution. That is, the randomizing and lowering of electron velocities produced by frequent encounters with the ions tends to impose the Boltzmann statistics upon the electrons. On the other hand, if the electron-ion collisions are so infrequent that the electrons can acquire substantial energy increase between them, the fastest electrons can absorb a disproportionate share of the energy and "run away." In this situation the energy gain far exceeds any of the losses, and in a laboratory plasma these electrons are generally found colliding with container walls.

Of course, such "runaway" electrons are of no value in adding energy to the plasma ions; to produce a plasma of high ion and electron temperature, such a condition for the electrons must be avoided. However, as the electron temperature is raised, ion-electron collisions become less frequent and are thus increasingly ineffective in transferring energy from electrons to ions. In addition, the decreased collision frequency causes the resistivity to drop, thereby decreasing the energy dissipation brought about by a given current density.

The maximum ion temperature attainable by ohmic heating thus depends upon the length of time that a relatively slow rate of electron heating can be carried out. This time is generally limited by instabilities, and it seems unlikely that ion temperatures in excess of the order of 1 keV can be attained without special precautions to contain the plasma. (One keV equals 10^3 eV.) For temperatures well below this level, ohmic heating provides a relatively straightforward heating technique.

Magnetic compression provides the possibility of increasing the ion temperatures directly. Magnetic compression of a plasma is brought about by increasing the magnetic field that surrounds the plasma. This increase causes the volume occupied by the plasma to decrease, and the particle energies are increased by the compression.

Evidently, magnetic compression of a plasma is similar to compression of a gas by a piston.

In fact, the similarity is sufficiently close that if a cylindrical plasma is radially compressed by a magnetic field, slowly and without loss of particles, the temperature T is related to the volume V by

$$TV^{\gamma-1} = \text{a constant}, \tag{3-16}$$

as also holds for an adiabatic gas compression. γ is the ratio of specific heats at constant pressure and volume for the compressed gas. When the compression is so slow that collisions are able to keep the velocity distribution of the particles randomized, $\gamma = \frac{5}{3}$ as for a monatomic gas. From Eq. 3-16 we see that as the compression proceeds and the volume decreases, the temperature rises.

Various arrangements may be made to accomplish the required compression. The pinch, discussed in § 2-1, produces compression as the current is increased. To see how the compression occurs, we note that the increasing current produces larger azimuthal fields about the plasma and that the plasma-vacuum interface shown in Fig. 2-3 will move inward until the sum of plasma and internal magnetic field pressures equals that exerted by the external magnetic field. The compression first adds a component of velocity to the particles in a direction perpendicular to the field increase, but particle collisions soon randomize these directed velocity increases. Compression of plasma is also possible within magnetic mirrors that have increasing magnetic fields. In this case the plasma is subject not only to a radial compression, but also to an axial compression.

In spite of end losses in the linear pinch the average particle energy is increased by the compression. However, the torroidal pinch, in which a large circulating current is induced into a torus of plasma, does not suffer such end losses and is therefore closer to the case represented by Eq. 3-16. Figure 3-5 shows how currents may be induced into such a plasma by making the torus the secondary winding of a transformer. A pulse applied to the transformer primary will induce a voltage around the torus and thereby cause the current to flow.

Ordinary gas dynamic shock waves provide another means whereby plasmas can be heated. When the waves occur within

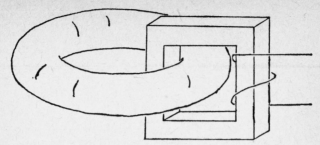

FIG. 3-5   The induction of current in a toroidal plasma.

magnetic fields, the shocks are generally hydromagnetic. In such cases the magnetic field of the shock contributes to the plasma compression.

The preceding discussion of magnetic compression heating has been directed to a "one-shot" process. That is, the plasma is thought of as being compressed and heated by one nonrepetitive build-up of the magnetic field. This "one-shot" process is not necessarily the most effective procedure for heating a plasma. An alternative method is to alternately compress and expand the plasma by use of an oscillating magnetic field. As the magnetic field increases, the plasma is compressed; as it decreases, the plasma expands. Under certain conditions this process is not thermodynamically reversible, and a net heating of the plasma results. Heating of a plasma by such a process is called *magnetic pumping*.

The efficiency with which a plasma can be heated by magnetic pumping turns out to be dependent upon the relationships among the magnetic field oscillation period, the ion collision time, and the ion transit time across the region over which the oscillating magnetic field is applied. These times are all generally much greater than the cyclotron period of the particles.

If the oscillation period and collision times are comparable and much less than the transit times, the particles on the average undergo a collision for each cycle of the magnetic field. In this way the directed velocity that was added to the particle to increase its energy is quickly shared with the other degrees of freedom by the collision process. Once the added velocity is randomized, it cannot be wholly withdrawn from the plasma by a subsequent expansion.

However, even if the ions suffer no collisions as they pass through the region of field change (that is, if the oscillation and transit times are comparable and much less than the collision time), energy is still transferred irreversibly from the oscillating field to the plasma since the heated particles do not spend all of their time within the field region. While outside the pumping region, collisions may remove some of the transverse energy added by pumping. Calculations have shown that the heating rate by this arrangement increases with ion temperature whereas that of the first case cited above does not. Thus the latter, called the transit time heating, is much favored for the temperatures of interest to thermonuclear research. The frequency for such magnetic pumping needs to be of the order of 10^5 cycles per sec.

Another means whereby electromagnetic energy may be added directly to the ions of a plasma is *ion cyclotron resonance heating*. In this process electromagnetic waves at the ion cyclotron frequency are induced into the plasma in such a way that waves can transfer much of their energy to the ions. The principle is much the same as in the cyclotron ion accelerator except that the ions in this case are accelerated within the plasma that supports the waves from which the ions draw their energy.

To begin, consider an ion located in the uniform magnetic field shown in Fig. 3-6. If the ion has any velocity, it will gyrate about the magnetic field direction at the ion cyclotron frequency given by Eq. 1-17, $\omega_{ci} = eB/M$. Application of an electric field at the cyclotron frequency by means of the parallel plates shown will cause

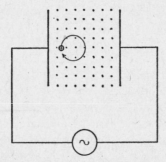

FIG. 3-6   Ion located in a magnetic field directed out of the figure and an oscillatory electric field between the plates.

the ion to be accelerated. The oscillating electric field will change its direction as the ion completes each half circle of its motion and thus will continuously accelerate the ion, causing it to gyrate with increasing radius of curvature. In a cylindrical geometry like that shown in Fig. 3-7 the accelerating electric field can be induced by

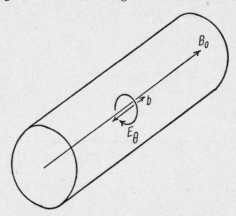

FIG. 3-7 Superposition of an oscillatory field b upon a steady field B_0 in a cylindrical geometry. The oscillatory field b induces the azimuthal electric field E_θ.

superimposing an oscillating component upon the axial magnetic field. The induced oscillating electric field will then be azimuthal. At a given location within the plasma the acceleration will proceed in much the same manner as that shown in Fig. 3-6.

For an isolated ion the foregoing procedure can clearly produce accelerations, but in a plasma the result is not so evident. In the first place, it is not obvious that the ion cyclotron motions, being in phase, do not act to exclude the driving electric field in a manner analogous to the collective motion of electrons at the plasma frequency. In the cylindrical case the screening action would indeed occur were it not for the axial motion of the plasma electrons that neutralize the oscillatory radial space charge set up by the collectively gyrating ions. In actual operation, hydromagnetic waves are propagated in a cylindrical geometry along a spatially decreasing magnetic field. As the field intensity is lowered to that required to bring the wave and ion cyclotron frequencies into resonance, the hydromagnetic waves become circularly polarized, as discussed in § 2-3. The electric field of these waves can then act to accelerate the ions at their cyclotron frequency. The energy thus added to the ions is highly directed, and the ions gyrate in phase. However, the collisions between ions, until now neglected in this discussion, are essential in converting this directed energy into random ion motions. The plasma electrons are not appreciably heated by the wave fields. They gain energy primarily by collisions with the ions. Of course, plasma electrons can be heated by application of electromagnetic fields at their cyclotron frequency.

§ 3-3 **Some Plasma Diagnostic Techniques.** A wide variety of diagnostic techniques are used to study the properties of laboratory and astrophysical plasmas. Each technique takes advantage of particular aspects of the plasma behavior. Some utilize the radiations given off by the plasma, some sample the plasma particles, others determine the effect of the plasma upon beams of radiation that interact with it.

The primary quantities to be known about a plasma are the electron, ion, and neutral particle temperatures and densities. Of great importance is whether or not the plasma is actually close to local thermodynamic equilibrium as required for the validity of most statistical predictions. Under some of the conditions discussed in §§ 3-1 and 3-2 the ionization is complete and the ions and electrons are close to thermal equilibrium. This situation is far from universal, however, and separate measures of each of the mentioned quantities is ordinarily required. Of course, the point in measuring these particular properties is that, at least in principle, once they are known a wide range of plasma properties may be deduced in terms of them. The actual situation is often not so simple, and much of experimental plasma physics is devoted to clarifying those cases where the theory cannot bridge the gap between a knowledge of the plasma parameters and boundary conditions and a predicted behavior. It is not our intention to describe a wide range of experimental techniques, but to concentrate upon a few that are more or less representative.

For a fully ionized plasma the resistivity given by Eq. 2-9 often provides a ready means of determining the electron temperature. The resistivity measured either along the direction of an applied magnetic field or in the absence of such a field is given by Eq. 2-9 in terms of the electron temperature T_e as

$$\eta = \frac{9.5 \times 10^{-2}}{T_e^{3/2}} \text{ ohm-cm}, \qquad (3\text{-}17)$$

where T_e is in eV. When the energy for a discharge is supplied by electrodes connected to a completely ionized plasma, the electrode voltage and current yield a value for the resistivity when the geometry of the discharge is known. The technique can also be used where an induced voltage and current can be made to flow in the plasma. Here again the voltage, current, and plasma geometry can be used to deduce the resistivity and thereby the electron temperature.

A small wire or plate, called a *Langmuir probe*, inserted into a plasma can under certain circumstances yield accurate values of the ion and electron densities and the electron temperature. When the voltage applied to a Langmuir probe is varied with respect to that of one of the discharge electrodes, the probe current is observed to have a dependence upon the probe voltage like that shown in Fig. 3-8. Certain plasma characteristics can be determined from the shape of such a plot.

When the probe voltage is made highly negative, only ions are collected, the electrons having insufficient energy to overcome the barrier due to the applied voltage. The current I_i collected at

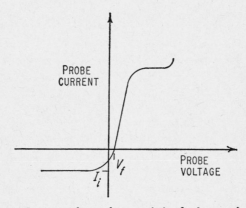

FIG. 3-8 Current-voltage characteristic of a Langmuir probe.

this negative potential is a direct result of the probe's interception of the random motions of the plasma ions. This current is proportional to the ion density in the plasma.

The application of increasingly positive voltages to the probe will allow electrons to be collected. Thus the net current is progressively diminished until at $V = V_f$ the ion and electron currents are equal and the net current is zero. V_f is called the *floating potential* and is the voltage which the probe would assume if it were not connected via external circuits to any voltage source.

At higher positive potentials, electron collection increases and eventually predominates. For all positive potentials the probe is surrounded by a sheath of electrons that are attracted to the region. This sheath presents a space charge barrier that inhibits further electron collection. However, as the probe is made more positive the increased electric field is instrumental in providing the energy whereby more and more electrons can overcome the sheath space charge and be collected by the probe. The shape of the voltage-current characteristic in this electron collection region is a direct result of the energy distribution of the electrons in the plasma. If the electrons satisfy a Boltzmann distribution, the probability that an electron has energy eV adequate to overcome a voltage V is $\exp(-eV/kT_e)$. Thus the number of electrons collected by the probe, n_p, is related to the plasma electron density, n_e, by $n_p = n_e \exp(-eV/kT)$, where $V = V_s - V_p$ is the difference between the sheath and probe potentials. Since the probe electron current I_e is proportional to the electron collection rate,

$$I_e \propto \exp[-e(V_s - V_p)/kT_e]. \qquad (3\text{-}18)$$

Taking the logarithm of this equation, it is evident that a plot of $\ln I_e$ vs V_p will yield a straight line with the slope e/kT_e. Thus the electron temperature can be determined. If the electrons do not satisfy a Boltzmann energy distribution, the $\ln I_e$ vs V_p plot will of course not yield a straight line.

Further increases of the probe voltage will ultimately provide a probe current that is proportional to the electron density in the plasma, since the effect of the sheath can be entirely counteracted and all electrons with paths that are intercepted by the probe are collected. As this point is reached, the increase of probe current will cease.

Sometimes other processes, such as thermal electron emission by the probe and ionization by probe-accelerated electrons, interfere with and modify the idealized probe characteristic shown in Fig. 3-8. In these cases the probe measurements may be unreliable. Implicit in the use of probes of any sort is the assumption that the plasma is essentially unmodified by the presence of the probe. Further, in order for us to use kinetic theory arguments to deduce the constants relating ion and electron currents to their corresponding densities, the probe must have dimensions that are large compared to a mean scattering length.

Langmuir probes can be used in the presence of a magnetic field, but very much more care must be exercised in interpreting the measurements than is indicated by this discussion.

Microwave techniques can be used in various ways to measure plasma electron density. The term microwave is used to designate electromagnetic radiation with wavelengths in the millimeter and centimeter range, that is, with frequencies from 3–300×10^9 cycles/sec. In § 2-3 we noted that electromagnetic waves were not transmitted by a plasma when the wave frequency was less than the plasma frequency. Below this frequency the electrons are able to move fast enough to follow the changes in the alternating electric field and thus inhibit transmission. Thus the plasma frequency can be measured by noting the frequency below which electromagnetic waves are "cut off," that is, not transmitted by the plasma. Since the plasma frequency is given by $\omega_p = (4\pi n_e e^2/m)^{1/2}$, its measurement immediately provides the electron density n_e. In a nonuniform plasma the cutoff occurs at the plasma frequency corresponding to the maximum electron density. Thus it is this maximum density that is measured in such cases.

Inserting appropriate values for the constants, the cutoff frequency is given by

$$f(\text{cutoff}) = 9.0 \times 10^3 n_e^{1/2} \text{ cycles/sec.} \qquad (3\text{-}19)$$

For most laboratory plasmas the cutoff frequency is in the microwave region. Thus if $n_e = 10^{14}$ cm^{-3}, $f(\text{cutoff})$ is nearly 10^{11} cycles/sec. This frequency is close to the upper limit that can be produced conveniently by high frequency oscillator tubes.

Microwaves can be used to measure electron density in another way. Instead of measuring the cutoff frequency, we can determine the phase shift of waves transmitted by the plasma. In § 2-3 we noted from Eq. 2-23 that the phase velocity for electromagnetic waves in a plasma was given by $c_p = c/[1 - (\omega_p/\omega)^2]^{1/2}$, where c is the velocity of light in a vacuum. Thus we see that a measure of the phase velocity, or what is equivalent, the phase shift over a given plasma path, can be used to deduce the plasma frequency ω_p and hence the electron density. To make the phase shift measurement a microwave interferometer like that shown in Fig. 3-9

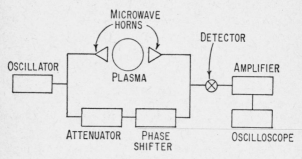

FIG. 3-9   A microwave interferometer.

is used. Here the output of a single microwave oscillator is taken by two alternate paths to a detector. One path, via the attenuator and phase shifter, is fixed and establishes a reference phase at the detector. The other path goes via microwave horns through the plasma under investigation. When the two signals are recombined at the detector, they will add constructively or destructively depending upon the relative phase shifts interposed into the two paths. If the attenuator and phase shifter are adjusted to give equal phase shifts and amplitudes via the two paths when the plasma is removed, the amplitude of the output from the detector can be used to indicate the phase shift caused by introduction of the plasma.

In practice the plasma density is often such that a phase shift corresponding to several wavelengths is introduced by the plasma. Then it becomes necessary to keep track of the number of full wavelength phase shifts corresponding to the maxima and minima of output voltage produced when the plasma is introduced between the microwave horns.

The spectral analysis of the radiations given off by a plasma can be a ready source of information about its state. The variety of measurements and techniques that are useful under various circumstances is quite large. To enable the reader to get some flavor of the content of such spectroscopic measurements, a description of an actual set of these observations will be given. It is very important to note that the particular techniques described are far from universally applicable and by no means exhaust the spectroscopic techniques that could be applied even in this one example.

We shall consider a highly ionized, decaying hydrogen plasma with particle densities of the order of 5×10^{15} cm^{-3} and temperatures of $1-4 \times 10^4$ °K. The method of formation of this particular plasma is such that the electron and ion temperatures are expected to be equal, as are their densities. Both the temperature and density can be obtained in a variety of ways from the hydrogen recombination spectrum radiated by the plasma.

Figure 1-7 shows a simplified energy-level diagram for hydrogen. Only the lower energy levels are shown; the higher levels nearer to the $W = 0$ level are more and more closely spaced. From this energy diagram we see that 13.6 eV are required to ionize a hydrogen atom from its lowest (ground state) energy level. Conversely, the recombination of an ion and electron to the ground state from the $W = 0$ ionization level will be accompanied by the release of a photon of energy 13.6 eV, or of wavelength 913 Ångstroms. Electrons of energy greater than zero will on recombining cause the emission of a continuum of radiated photons with energies greater than 13.6 eV and wavelengths correspondingly shorter.

In a completely ionized hydrogen plasma all of the electrons will have greater than zero energy. When such a plasma recombines, the electrons are captured by the ions into all the various energy levels below $W = 0$. As they do so, radiation at wavelengths corresponding to the electron energy loss is emitted. The electrons of zero energy recombine to the atomic energy levels, and radiation at discrete wavelength is emitted. When this radiation is analyzed using a spectrograph, lines are observed at various wavelengths. These spectral lines occur in various *series* called Lyman, Balmer, Paschen, etc., referring to recombination to the $n = 1, 2, 3$ levels, respectively. Successive Balmer lines are called H$_\alpha$, H$_\beta$, H$_\gamma$, etc., corresponding to decay from the $n = 3, 4, 5$ levels respectively.

Superimposed upon the line radiation are continuum radiations corresponding to recombination to each of the levels by electrons having energy greater than zero.

In addition to simple recombination, all plasma atoms are subject to reionization by collision and other processes. Thus at any given time during the plasma decay the various states are variously populated and depopulated by the excitation and radiative events. At a particular temperature the populations of the states will be given by the Saha equation, Eq. 1-40, if the plasma is in local thermodynamic equilibrium, that is, if the populating and depopulating processes very nearly balance.

Since the radiations, both line and continuum, are the result of recombination of ions and electrons, the intensities are closely proportional to the product of ion density n_i and electron density n_e in the plasma. Thus a measure of the absolute intensity of any of the radiations when combined with known recombination rates can be used to determine the product $n_e n_i$. The two densities are essentially equal for a plasma; therefore the absolute intensity measurements determine either density uniquely. In this discussion it is assumed for simplicity that none of the radiations used in the analysis is self-absorbed by the plasma.

Of course, the intensity of the radiation at the various lines and continua is dependent upon the electron temperature. For most transitions in a plasma with electron temperature above about 10,000°K the recombination rate decreases with increasing temperature, but the temperature dependence of the rate is by no means the same for all transitions. For example, the temperature dependence of the intensity in a narrow band around 5300 Å in the continuum resulting from capture to the $n = 2$ state varies by only about 25 percent from $T_e \approx 10,000°K$ to $T_e \approx 100,000°K$. On the other hand, a band at 3200 Å in the continuum of the $n = 1$ state varies by a factor of five over the same temperature range, and the H_β line intensity by a factor of nearly 50.

Since the various intensities are all very nearly proportional to $n_e n_i$ and have widely differing temperature dependences, it is obvious that the ratio of two intensities can be used as a density-independent measure of the temperature. Furthermore, once the electron temperature is determined from such a ratio the density can be deduced from an absolute intensity measurement. Of course, in order that any error in the temperature measurement not be strongly reflected in the density determination, it is advisable to use the absolute intensity of radiation for which the temperature dependence is as small as possible. The continuum radiation emitted in transition to the $n = 2$ state in the neighborhood of 5300 Å is well suited to this purpose.

To analyze plasma in this manner it is useful to follow its time behavior as it decays. To do so, it is only necessary to determine the time dependence of the requisite line and continuum intensities. This can be done by use of spectrometers equipped with rapidly responding photomultiplier tube outputs.

In this manner a plot of the electron density and the electron temperature with time as a parameter can be constructed for a particular plasma and compared to that predicted from the Saha equation based upon local thermodynamic equilibrium. Figure 3-10 is such a plot for a particular laboratory plasma that has been analyzed. The boxes represent the various measured temperatures and densities with the box size reflecting the measurement errors. The numbers appended to each box are the times at which the

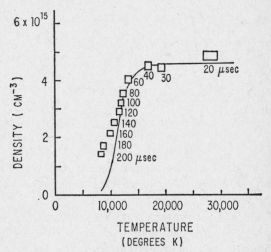

FIG. 3-10 Ion density as a function of electron temperature for a particular decaying plasma.

particular measurement was made in microseconds after the start of the discharge. The solid line connects a set of temperatures and densities calculated from Saha's equation for a plasma at a density of about 4.6×10^{15} cm^{-3}. It is seen that the plasma cools for about 40μsec to about 1.7×10^4 °K before appreciable recombination takes place. Then recombination begins, and the plasma continues in local thermodynamic equilibrium until 120μsec or so. After this time the collisional processes are no longer adequate to balance the radiative ones for the n = 1 and n = 2 levels involved in the measurement, and local thermodynamic equilibrium fails to hold. Much more complicated arguments than those needed to determine the Saha equation are necessary to account for these later measurements.

§ 3-4 **Some Laboratory Experiments.** A wide variety of plasma experiments have been performed to aid in the understanding of plasmas. As we have already seen, plasmas are governed by the well-established fundamentals of atomic physics, electromagnetic theory, and statistical mechanics. However, the extremely complicated manner in which these "well-known" fundamentals combine to yield an accurate description of plasma behavior is far from clear. In such a situation, new and previously unsuspected relationships are often first found experimentally. Furthermore, approximations are usually very helpful in shaping our understanding of plasma, and it is generally evident that experiments provide essential evidence as to which approximations are appropriate.

The experiments that are described in this section are selected from but two general areas of plasma research: the positive column of glow discharges, and wave propagations in highly ionized plasmas. The selection of these two areas is entirely arbitrary, except that they happen to represent certain interests of the author. The scope and depth of experimental investigations is barely suggested by these samples, but perhaps a bit of the flavor can be discerned.

The first set of experiments is concerned in one way or another with the positive column of a glow discharge. Thus the discussion of § 3-1 is closely related to that which follows.

The first experiment involves the interaction of electromagnetic waves and plasma at frequencies close to the plasma frequency.

We have seen from the dispersion relations of § 2-3 that for fre-
quencies below the plasma frequency given by Eq. 1-11, $\nu_p = (ne^2/\pi m)^{1/2}$, the plasma will not transmit, but reflects, incident
electromagnetic waves. In the early 1930's Tonks performed ex-
periments which demonstrated this resonance effect in the positive
column of a cylindrical mercury discharge tube. In § 1-1 we saw
why such a resonance should occur: the electron mass and charge
provide the inertia and retarding force, respectively, for the oscillation. However, in addition to the resonance at the plasma
frequency, other resonances were observed. Tonks ascribed the
additional resonances to the nonuniform electron density expected
in the column because of diffusion effects like those described in
connection with Eq. 3-14. But he did not give a theoretical justifi-
cation of the suggestion.

These experiments were repeated during the 1950's using microwaves with wavelengths from 3 cm to 30 cm. These later experiments were performed both in free space and within microwave
waveguides. The free space experiments are relatively more complex because the details of the interaction of the microwaves with
transmitting and receiving antennae become important. In addition, the practical problem of finding a "free-space" environment
is not altogether trivial since reflections from nearby objects can
be a source of confusion.

On the other hand, the propagation of microwaves in a guide is
very well controlled and the guide provides a suitable environment
for the experiment. The experimental arrangement used to study
the resonance in a waveguide is shown in Fig. 3-11. Here a discharge is struck between the two electrodes in the bulb end. Then
a positive column is formed inside the glass tube that traverses
the waveguide by application of a positive voltage to the electrode
at the other end of the tube. With the microwave electric vector
perpendicular to the plasma column, the plasma electron oscillations are evidently also perpendicular to the column axis.

In microwave experiments of this type it is not always convenient
to vary the wave frequency. Thus to observe the resonances it is
often useful to vary the electron density. This variation can be
readily made by changing the current in the positive column. As
the current is increased, the electron density increases, and the

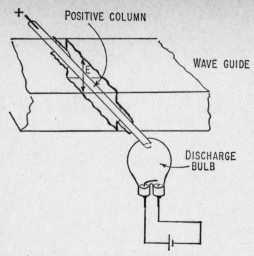

FIG. 3-11 Experimental arrangement for studying plasma resonances in a cylindrical plasma located in a microwave guide. The primary discharge is maintained in the discharge bulb, and a positive column is formed within the glass tube that traverses the wave guide.

plasma frequency at any point in the column is also increased. Microwave power is transmitted down the guide; when there is no discharge in the tube, the microwaves are scarcely perturbed by the tube itself. However, the situation is entirely different when the positive column traverses the guide. When the power reflected by the plasma column is plotted as a function of the positive column current, the dependence shown in Fig. 3-12 is obtained.

The current marked I_0 corresponds roughly to the electron density near the column wall where the plasma frequency at that region would equal that of the applied microwaves. The problem, left unresolved by Tonks, was to account for the other resonances observed.

An important recent finding is that for a given discharge tube the number and spacings of the resonances can be varied, but that there is a particular value of current below which no resonance is observed. Experiments performed in free space (not in a waveguide) indicated that these other resonances are, like the primary one, dipole. That is, they are produced by the simple linear oscilla-

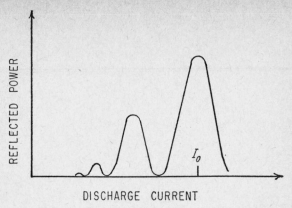

FIG. 3-12 Dependence of power reflected upon the current passed by a positive column of a mercury discharge in an arrangemnt like that shown in Fig. 3-11.

tion of the column electrons, and at large distance they produce a field pattern like that expected from a harmonically oscillating line charge.

As a result of detailed experiments in which the electron temperature, density, tube diameter, and applied frequency were varied, it is generally concluded that the nonuniform electron density does in fact account for the multiple resonances. This effect is thought to act in the following manner:

From Eq. 3-14 the electron density distribution is expected to appear as shown in Fig. 3-13a. Due to a less than infinite recombination rate at the wall, the density near the wall has the value n_0. When microwaves are incident upon this column, they produce a resonance when the wave frequency $\nu = (n_0 e^2 / \pi m)^{1/2}$. At this frequency the microwaves do not penetrate the plasma, but are reflected by the outer boundary. Reflection at this boundary is thought to produce the peak labeled I_0 in Fig. 3-12. If the frequency is held constant and the over-all electron density profile is decreased by reducing the positive column current, the microwaves penetrate beyond the column wall. Reflection at the reduced currents will occur at that column radius where the electron density is n_0.

As the radial position at which n_0 occurs moves inward, a point will finally be reached at which the total phase shift of the micro-

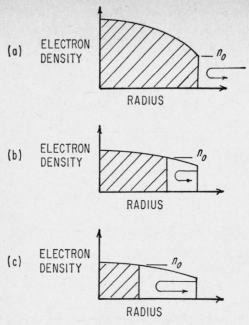

FIG. 3-13 Electron density profile of a positive column for an electron density n_0 at the boundary (a) and at two interior points (b) and (c).

waves in traveling from the outer boundary to the radial position of reflections will be π. This condition is shown in Fig. 3-13. Thus a standing wave should be established between the wall and the new resonant radius, and a resonance thereby produced. Further decrease of the column current depresses the electron density distribution even more, and finally another radius separated from the boundary by a phase shift of 2π acquires the electron density n_0 as shown in Fig. 3-13c. Finally, the electron density will be lowered so much that the density n_0 can exist only at or near the center of the column, and the last resonance is observed. The minimum current that can produce a resonance is fixed, as observed experimentally, and corresponds to the density n_0 at the center of the column. In this way the multiple resonances from a nonuniform plasma column have been interpreted.

A different set of experiments concerns the diffusion processes in a positive column. We have already noted in § 3-1 that the radial diffusion of the column electrons and ions to the tube wall is strongly influenced by the electrostatic fields set up by the diffusing electrons themselves. In Eq. 3-14 the radial distribution of electron density was written in terms of the ambipolar diffusion coefficient. Also it was noted that the radial diffusion of electrons should be retarded by a longitudinal magnetic field and the resulting space charge field set up by the electrons should retard ion diffusion. The stronger the field, the less the electrons and ions should be able to diffuse across it.

The longitudinal electric field in a positive column supplies the energy whereby the ionization processes can maintain the column against the various loss processes. When the field is such that the electrons can acquire sufficient energy between collisions to maintain their average energy and density against the losses, a steady state prevails. The magnitude of the electric field required to maintain a given electron density or column current thus serves as a monitor of the diffusion processes in the column. If a longitudinal magnetic field suppresses the radial diffusion of column ions and electrons, the power input required from the longitudinal electric field is lowered.

A number of experiments have been performed to determine the reduction in the diffusion coefficient caused by relatively low values of longitudinal magnetic field. These experiments are performed with apparatus similar to that shown in Fig. 3-1 except that care must be taken to make the discharge tube very long compared to its diameter. Otherwise, the true radial diffusion is strongly masked by the flow of electrons and ions along magnetic field lines to the conducting electrode, thereby neutralizing the radial electric space charge field. The increased diffusion caused by this short-circuiting effect is called Simon diffusion. It can be made negligible if sufficiently large ratios of length-to-diameter discharge tubes are used. For fields of a few hundred gauss, the longitudinal electric field for constant current decreases monotonically with increasing field, and the effective diffusion coefficient is found to be related to the ambipolar coefficient, as indicated in § 3-1.

However, additional experiments have shown that as the magnetic field is increased further, the monotonic decrease of longitudinal electric field is abruptly reversed. The "critical" magnetic field at which the electric field begins to increase is of the order of 1 kG. This electric field increase, of course, signals an increase in radial diffusion. When first observed, it caused some concern as to its origin. An examination of the time and space dependence of the column's luminosity turned out to be extremely useful in clarifying the mechanism of the enhanced diffusion. With the aid of fast cameras and phototube devices, an instability of the positive column in the form of a helix is observed to form at the critical field. The instability causes the plasma of the column to be located closer to the outside walls of the tube, thus enhancing the radial diffusion.

To understand how such an instability could arise, it is easy to imagine that very small radial displacements of the positive column can spontaneously occur. For example, a small inhomogeneity could slightly shift the region of maximum current conduction. If the longitudinal magnetic field is sufficiently low that diffusion processes can readily smooth out and dissipate these small displacements of the column, nothing further can occur. However, if the field is strong enough to inhibit their dissipation, the forces on the column exerted by the magnetic field upon the radial components of the column current can cause displacement to grow. An initial radial displacement midway along the positive column will create radial components in the column current that are directed outward on one side of the displacement and inward on the other as shown in Fig. 3-14. When these radial components of current interact with the magnetic field B, they are twisted by the forces F_θ into a helix. The helix has an azimuthal current component j_θ. The interaction of this component with B will produce the radial force F_r which drives the helix to the wall of the discharge tube.

An apparent rotation of the helix that is also observed can be understood in terms of the electron drift motion that is opposite to the current j shown. When each element of the helix moves with this longitudinal drift velocity, the helix will, indeed, appear to rotate. The apparent rotation of the luminous helix is probably not associated with any actual mass motion of the plasma, but likely corresponds to the progress of the region of increased ionization through various portions of the column. It is evident that

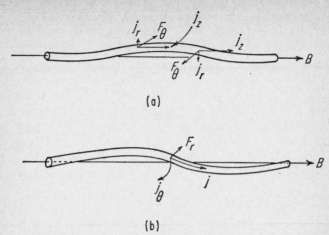

(a)

(b)

FIG. 3-14. The development of a helical instability in a positive column subject to a longitudinal magnetic field.

regardless of the direction in which the original displacement occurs, the helix will always be wrapped around the field lines in the clockwise sense when viewed along the direction of the field. The direction of the apparent rotation of the helix and of the electron drift are observed to agree with this sense.

For certain specific forms of perturbation of the positive column electron density, it has been possible to deduce a dispersion relation for propagation of the perturbation. In particular, the critical magnetic field, the wavelength of the helix, and its frequency of rotation as functions of gas pressure, column current, and other parameters have been calculated. Observed values are in reasonable agreement with those deduced by this perturbation approach in spite of the fact that the instability is ordinarily observed only long after its onset while the theory is concerned only with the initial development of the perturbation.

The experiments described above are concerned with the plasma in the positive column of a glow discharge. As noted in § 3-1, these plasmas are not highly ionized, and many types of hydromagnetic effects are not generally demonstrable in them. The hydromagnetic wave experiments to be discussed next are best performed in more highly ionized plasma.

Alfvén waves are a particularly interesting and simple form of hydromagnetic wave. As discussed in § 2-3, these waves are transverse in character and do not, at small amplitudes, markedly affect the plasma pressure. They are, therefore, linear phenomena and propagate at the velocity given in Eq. 2-28:

$$V_A = B_0/(4\pi\rho)^{1/2}, \tag{3-20}$$

where B_0 is the steady magnetic field along which the Alfvén waves propagate and ρ is the mass density of the propagating medium. The wave magnetic field is perpendicular to B_0, and the resultant form of the field for these waves is as shown in Fig. 2-13.

Early attempts to observe these waves were made in liquid metals before high density plasmas were available. The first experiments were done in mercury. Later, liquid sodium was used because of its higher conductivity and lower density and in spite of substantial handling difficulties. In the early experiments the mercury was contained in a circular stainless steel cylinder at the bottom of which was located a multivaned paddle wheel. A magnetic field of 13 000 gauss was applied in the axial direction of the cylinder. Oscillation of the paddle wheel was expected to produce azimuthal displacements of the mercury near it.

The conductivity of the mercury prevented it from moving with complete freedom with respect to the magnetic field. It was thus expected that torsional Alfvén waves would be produced by the coupled action of the mercury and the magnetic field. These waves would then propagate up to the free surface, where they would be reflected. Standing waves would be produced except that dissipation effects are so large in mercury that severe attenuation of the waves is expected.

Detection of the attenuated waves was attempted by observing the perturbations of the free surface as they were coupled to a mirror arrangement floating on the surface. In both the mercury and the liquid sodium experiments the attenuation of the waves was so severe that a standing wave resonance was not well resolved.

More recently, highly ionized plasmas have become readily available. It has therefore been possible to carry out well-controlled experiments with these Alfvén waves. Figure 3-15 shows the apparatus that was used in one of these studies. The geometry is

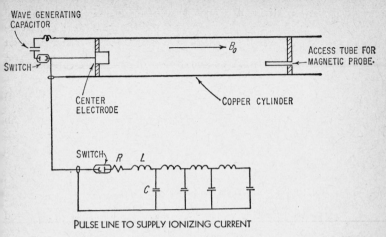

FIG. 3-15   Apparatus used to demonstrate the propagation of Alfvén waves in a hydrogen plasma.

essentially the same as that used in the conducting liquid experiments; the only modifications are those required for handling a plasma rather than a liquid. The plasma, formed by discharge of the pulse line shown, is contained in a copper cylinder the ends of which are closed by insulating plates. A magnetic field is directed along the axis of the cylinder. After the plasma is formed, the hydromagnetic waves are induced by connecting a charged capacitor between the outside cylinder and the coaxial center electrode. The oscillatory discharge of the capacitor causes a radial current to flow between the electrode and the cylinder. The interaction of this current with the axial magnetic field produces a torsional oscillation of the plasma. The high conductivity effectively couples the plasma to the field, and the torsional waves propagate along the axial field. The wave frequency was selected to be sufficiently low so that Eq. 3-20 is expected to hold.

Small magnetic pickup loops inserted into tubes that enter the plasma from the opposite end of the cylinder are used to detect the propagated waves. The principal wave magnetic field component is in the azimuthal direction, and suitably oriented pickup loops located at various axial positions can be used to determine the velocity and attenuation of the wave. Using such an arrangement, the variation of phase velocity with magnetic field was measured and found to agree with the predictions based upon Eq. 3-20.

Many further details of hydromagnetic wave propagation in plasma have been observed using experimental arrangements similar to that shown. In particular, wave amplitude attenuation and the complications added by varying the wave frequency with respect to the various particle resonances have been partially explored. As the wave frequency approaches the ion cyclotron frequency, this mode of wave propagation is strongly attenuated as the wave energy is transferred to the gyrating ions.

When the wave amplitude is not small compared to the axial field, nonlinear effects result. Of great interest in this connection is the steepening of the wave fronts that should arise in the manner of a shock wave formation. For large amplitude waves the velocity is no longer given by Eq. 3-20. Instead, the plasma compressibility begins to play a role. This causes the wave velocity to be dependent upon the instantaneous amplitude of the wave magnetic field. The phase velocity according to Eq. 2-50 becomes

$$c_p = \left[\frac{B_0{}^2 + b(t)^2}{4\pi\rho} \right]^{1/2}, \qquad (3\text{-}21)$$

where $b(t)$ is the time-dependent wave amplitude. We see that this expression reduces to Eq. 3-20 in the limit as $b \ll B_0$. Since Eq. 3-21 implies that the larger portions of the wave should travel faster than those of low amplitude, the wave maxima should tend to overtake the lower amplitude portions, thus steepening the wave fronts. This steepening should continue until dissipation processes limit it.

Experiments designed to observe the steepening of the wave front have been performed, using an arrangement like that shown in Fig. 3-15. Using an axial field of 8000 gauss, the wave amplitudes were varied from about 500–5000 gauss and the increase in slope of the wave front observed. For propagation distances up to 20 cm the waves were observed to steepen as expected, but beyond this distance dissipation mechanisms prohibited the further development of a shock front. The rapid increase with wave frequency of the wave energy losses due to charge exchange between ions and neutrals in the steepened waves of this experiment possibly accounted for the inhibition of further shock development.

Besides the torsional waves discussed above, there are a number of other modes of hydromagnetic wave propagations. One of these is the so-called fast mode. This mode can also be induced in a cylindrical plasma, like that described above. In this case, a single-turn loop of wire is wound around one end of the discharge chamber, which must now be an insulator. An oscillating current passed through this loop will locally modulate the steady longitudinal magnetic field B_0. The principal magnetic component of the wave field produced is b_z. This wave will propagate along the direction of B_0 according to a dispersion relation that yields the phase velocities

$$c_p = \left(\frac{\omega}{\omega_{ci}}\right)^{1/2} V_A \text{ for } \omega_{ce} \gg \omega \gg \omega_{ci},$$

$$c_p = \omega \left[\frac{\omega^2}{V_A{}^2} - k_c{}^2\right]^{-1/2} \quad \text{for} \quad \omega \ll \omega_{ci}. \qquad (3\text{-}22)$$

Here ω and ω_{ci} are the angular wave and ion cyclotron frequencies, respectively. V_A is the Alfvén velocity, and k_c is a constant, with the dimensions of inverse length, that is determined by the geometry of the system. This mode is not cut off at the ion cyclotron frequency, but it cannot propagate when $\omega < k_c V_A$.

Experiments designed to test the dispersion relation for this mode have been performed. One experiment utilized an argon plasma in a glass discharge tube of 22 cm diameter and 200 cm length. The plasma was formed by a discharge between electrodes located at either end of the tube. Magnetic fields could be varied from 1 kG to 6 kG. Wave frequencies ranging from 200 kc/sec to 1 Mc/sec were used, allowing ω/ω_{ci} to be varied from 1.2 to 6. In this experiment the measurements of phase velocity and absorption coefficient were found to be in agreement with the dispersion relations calculated for this mode, and the cutoff below $\omega = k_c V_A$ was demonstrated.

The foregoing hydromagnetic wave experiments are but a few of those that have been performed. Taken together, these experiments give convincing evidence that available dispersion relations have wide ranges of validity.

§ 3-5 Controlled Thermonuclear Fusion Experiments.

The combination of two low-mass nuclei results in the release of energy. When a deuteron (d) combines with another deuteron, the energy release is either 3.25 MeV or 4 MeV, depending on which of the two reactions

$$d + d \rightarrow He^3 + n + 3.25 \text{ MeV}$$
$$d + d \rightarrow H^3 + p + 4 \text{ MeV}$$

occurs. The hydrogen bomb makes use of such fusion reactions to release enormous amounts of energy. The exploration of means to establish a controlled release of this energy is often called "controlled thermonuclear fusion research."

In such research a prime fact is that the Coulomb field of the reacting nuclei tends to keep them separated. Thus they do not interact unless they possess enough relative velocity to overcome the electrostatic repulsive force between them. This force has been overcome for decades in nuclear research by use of particle accelerators that impart large velocities to one set of nuclear particles, which then impinge upon a target containing the nuclei to be bombarded. Such accelerators do not operate with high enough efficiency to allow a net energy gain from thermonuclear reactions.

The thermonuclear reactions occur in the hydrogen bomb by virtue of the high temperature, hence high relative velocities, of the reacting nuclei. These temperatures are created in the bomb by first firing a conventional fission ("atomic") bomb. Such a violent triggering mechanism is not possible for a controlled thermonuclear reaction, and other means must be sought for attaining the necessary particle velocities.

Since these velocities correspond to energies of the order of 10^4 eV, that is, to temperatures of the order of 10^8 deg K, it is obvious that such controlled reactions cannot be produced within ordinary material containers. Thus the problem comes down to the need to maintain nuclear particles at these energies for times long enough to allow the fusion reactions to occur, but without the use of a material container. For some time it has been thought that the most likely direction in which progress could be made on this problem is to have the reacting particles be the positive ions of a high temperature plasma that, because of its electrical conductivity, could be confined by magnetic fields. Great effort has been expended to solve the problem in this way, and much that has been learned about plasmas, particularly high temperature ones, has come from studies that have been more or less closely motivated by this problem.

We have discussed in various earlier sections the problems of the heating and confinement of plasmas. No solutions to these problems are yet evident, but several avenues of approach have been developed. These include the use of the pinch effect, of various types of mirror confinement schemes, and of the so-called "stellarator." Some of these schemes are discussed here, but no attempt has been made to be all-inclusive. Although at a very early period there was some hope that a simple pinch discharge such as that shown in Fig. 2-3 or the toroidal one shown in Fig. 3-5 could produce sufficient heating and containment to allow thermonuclear reactions, the instabilities of these pinches were so gross as to exclude their use. Subsequently, various stabilization schemes have been developed to delay the onset of the instabilities. One stabilizing scheme provides a magnetic field trapped within the pinched plasma as shown in Fig. 2-7, and a highly conducting wall surrounding the plasma. Thus the internal field is intended to oppose tendencies toward the development of kinks and toward the pinching off of the plasma at constrictions. At the same time, the surrounding conductor limits the extent to which the kink instabilities develop by opposing the penetration of the azimuthal magnetic fields of the pinch current.

When these precautions are taken, the plasma pinch is still unstable in that there is an irregular, fine-scale fluttering of the plasma surface. It is not clear that this instability is inherent in the pinch, but there is evidence to indicate that it is related to the unintended but perhaps unavoidable introduction of impurities into the discharge. As with the other devices considered here, it is not yet clear that the pinch will be useful in producing a plasma that is adequate for thermonuclear power production.

We have already discussed the possible use of magnetic mirrors to confine a thermonuclear plasma. In large measure the mirror arrangement makes use of strong magnetic fields to prohibit the radial loss of plasma and also provides even stronger mirror fields to inhibit axial loss. As outlined in § 1-3, the mirrors are effective in containing only those particles with sufficiently high ratio of radial to axial momentum. Since the mirror geometry is not subject to some of the instabilities inherent in the pinch, it has been thought to be a more likely means of plasma containment where only the end losses need be compensated. Furthermore, the superposition of hexapole fields like that shown in Fig. 2-9 has increased hopes for a suitable mirror device.

One technique for heating plasma contained by a magnetic mirror is adiabatic compression. This method, outlined in § 3-3, is limited only by the extent to which the confining field can be raised. Attempts to test adiabatic compression have been made; one such experiment is called Toy Top. Figure 3-16 shows how this device is designed to operate. A burst of plasma was introduced at one end, as shown in Fig. 3-16a. The plasma was held and compressed within the first mirrors, then transferred to the second, where further compression occurs. Following this second compres-

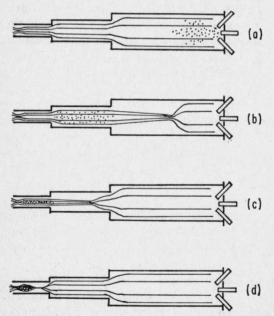

FIG. 3-16   Heating of plasma by a multiple compression device.

sion, the plasma was to be transferred to a third mirror of yet smaller radius for final compression. The point of the successive transfers is to allow higher and higher fields to be used without their having to act throughout the large volume of the first chamber. (The term Toy Top derived from the successive plasma compressions that were thought to resemble those imparted to toy tops to make them spin.)

Another proposed method of obtaining high temperature plasmas within a magnetic mirror is to inject large currents of particles at high energy and then to trap them within the mirrors. The mirrors are then supposed to contain the high energy particles long enough for thermonuclear reactions to occur. A primary problem of this scheme concerns the trapping of the high energy particles; at least two methods have been proposed.

In one method, called *DCX* (direct current experiment), a continuous beam of D_2^+ ions at several hundred kilovolts energy is injected into the mirror system shown in Fig. 3-17. To provide trapping, the D_2^+ ion trajectories are intersected by a high current arc discharge that dissociates the ions. Their ratio of charge to mass is thereby doubled, and their radius of curvature halved. The mirror geometry is arranged so that the new radius of curvature prevents the ions from leaving the system. The purpose of the mirror is thus to confine the high energy beam and background plasma until the directed energy has been thermalized and the contents of the device raised to thermonuclear energies.

Another method of injecting high energy particles into a mirror is to use neutral particles that are subsequently ionized and trapped. A particularly interesting ionization technique consists of passing

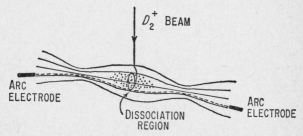

FIG. 3-17   The DCX high-energy beam injection and arc break-up system.

highly excited but neutral atoms through a steep magnetic field gradient. The gradient can induce an electric field that completes the ionization with considerable efficiency. It is intended that the high energy ions, once trapped, be contained by mirror or minimum B fields.

A problem in all mirror devices is the seemingly unavoidable end losses. A cylindrical device called *astron* has been conceived that largely eliminates such losses by providing a region of space about which all field lines are closed. In astron, relativistic electrons are injected so as to form a layer within a magnetic mirror field, as shown in Fig. 3-18. When the electrons are of sufficient density

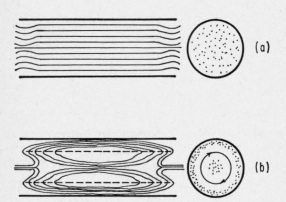

(a)

(b)

FIG. 3-18   The Astron device for containment and heating of plasma by a relativistic electron layer.

in this layer to provide a reversal of the applied magnetic field, the net field resembles that shown in Fig. 3-18b. It is seen from this figure that the magnetic field lines surrounding the electron layer are completely closed. If the relativistic electrons are then allowed to ionize and heat a plasma also contained by this closed magnetic field, thermonuclear temperatures are thought to be achievable. An essential question about astron concerns the stability of the electron layer; it is not known from operation of the device whether such a layer is maintained.

Yet another method of avoiding the end losses of mirror systems is to have a geometry with no ends. The torus mentioned before in connection with the pinch discharges is one such possibility. The stellarator to be described next is another. It might be thought that a successful endless geometry might be achieved by simply taking a long solenoidal magnetic field configuration and closing it upon itself to form a torus. Such a simple modification will not work. In any such case where the magnetic field lines are everywhere parallel to the confining walls the magnetic field will be weaker at outside walls of the torus than at the inside. This effect is obvious since the windings producing the magnetic field are perforce more closely spaced on the inside than on the outside of the torus. The resulting field gradient will cause the ions and electrons to drift with respect to each other, as outlined in § 1-3. The electric fields produced by the resulting charge separation will, in concert with the applied field, cause the plasma to be lost to the tube walls.

The basic concept of the *stellarator* is to provide a magnetic field configuration that will cause this charge separation to be neutralized. Evidently this can be accomplished if the magnetic lines that thread the torus are arranged so that they do not close on themselves after one revolution. Without this closure, particles are free to circulate throughout the entire interior of the torus without crossing field lines. This circulation substantially eases neutralization of any space charge that might develop. A magnetic field that does not close on itself for each revolution in the torus can be achieved if the principal displacement of the field lines is rotational. Such a magnetic field is said to have rotational transform.

A field of this type can be produced by a set of helical windings like those shown in Fig. 3-19a that are used in addition to those producing the solenoidal field. The transform is then achieved by arranging such a set of field windings in the form of a loop, as shown in Fig. 3-19b.

Various other specific devices and procedures are also important to the over-all stellarator concept. Among others is the use of a "diverter" to cleanse the plasma of impurity ions of high atomic number that could cool the plasma by radiation from electron capture and scattering. Plasma heating in the stellarator is planned to be by magnetic pumping and by ion cyclotron heating, as discussed in § 3-3.

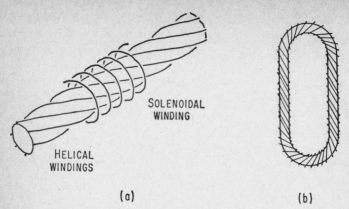

SOLENOIDAL
WINDING

HELICAL
WINDINGS

(a)

(b)

FIG. 3-19 Helical field windings (a) and toroidal device (b) for achieving rotational transform in the stellarator.

As already mentioned, none of these devices or others have succeeded in producing a plasma suitable for thermonuclear power production, although much information of great value to the accomplishment of this goal has been acquired. It remains clear that research on controlled thermonuclear devices is very promising and that it constitutes one of the exciting aspects of plasma research.

4 *Naturally Occurring Plasmas*

In extending the foregoing discussion of plasmas from laboratory to astrophysical systems, we must note several important differences. Foremost, of course, is the enormous change in linear scale. Whereas laboratory plasmas seldom have linear dimensions in excess of some meters, the influence of the solar plasma extends far beyond the earth's orbit, which has a radius of 1.5×10^{11} meters. Other regions in interstellar and perhaps intergalactic space are subject to plasma influences and are even larger in extent. An important effect of the change of scale is to allow the very dilute ionized material occupying these spaces to be treated as plasma. We see from Fig. 1-2 that in spite of very low electron densities in many of these regions, the Debye length remains short compared to the dimensions of the region.

Perhaps less striking, but equally important, are the time scales involved in the workings of astrophysical systems. Figure 1-2 shows electron plasma frequencies from about 10^8 to 10^{13} sec^{-1} for laboratory plasmas and from 10^8 down to 10^3 sec^{-1} and even below for cosmic systems. In interstellar regions the magnetic fields, although still exerting a powerful influence upon the plasma there, may fall to values of 10^{-5} gauss or below. Corresponding ion and electron cyclotron frequencies are thus reduced by factors of 10^9 or so below those in common laboratory plasmas. Of course, the changed space and time scales go together to characterize the exceedingly slow evolution, but gross dimensions of the cosmic systems.

Yet another difference between laboratory and astrophysical plasmas is the general absence of boundaries in the latter. In various laboratory plasmas, boundaries play a decisive role. Not only do they define the plasma volume, but they also control the electromagnetic fields and pressures acting upon the plasma. In the space beyond the earth's surface, boundaries in the laboratory sense do not exist, although in certain places more subtle types of boundaries are found.

This chapter is devoted to the naturally occuring plasmas. The first four sections describe the sun and its influence upon interplanetary space and, to a limited extent, the upper parts of planetary atmospheres. First, we shall discuss the magnetohydrodynamic workings of the sun itself. Then we shall see that the sun's influence is carried throughout interplanetary space by a very complicated interplay of solar magnetic fields and solar plasma emission. The constant "solar wind" of plasma, the interaction of that wind with the earth's magnetic field, and the solar perturbations of the wind will be used to discuss such diverse phenomena as magnetic storms, auroras, and cosmic ray fluctuations. Regions beyond the solar system are discussed in the last section.

§ 4-1 The Sun. To properly appreciate the influence of the sun upon the interplanetary plasma, and indeed to understand the workings of the sun itself, some acquaintance with the dimensions of the pertinent parts of the solar system is necessary. The sun's diameter is 1.4×10^6 kilometers (km), and it subtends an arc of about 0.5 degrees when viewed from the earth. Thus the sun-to-earth distance is about 120 solar diameters, or 1.5×10^8 km. This distance is called one astronomical unit (AU). The distance to Pluto, the most distant planet, is about 40 AU. The distance to which organized plasma motion from the sun extends is thought to be at least 50 AU; the entire solar system is affected by the solar plasma.

The behavior of the plasma in this region is ultimately governed by the sun itself; we begin by discussing it. Information about the solar surface is obtained by use of telescopes and spectrographs. A limit to the degree of detail that can be seen on the solar disc from the earth's surface is set by the earth's atmosphere at about one second of arc. On the solar surface this corresponds to about 1000 km. Observations from above the earth's atmosphere have considerably lowered this limit.

Since the outer layers of the sun are not in thermodynamic equilibrium, different methods of temperature measurement can yield differing values. However, an approximate measure of the surface temperature can be obtained from the Stefan-Boltzmann radiation law for the total observed energy output P:

$$P = \sigma A T^4. \tag{4-1}$$

Here σ ($= 5.67 \times 10^{-5}$ erg/cm^2 deg^4 sec) is the Stefan-Boltzmann constant, A is the solar surface area, and T is the equivalent black-body temperature needed to provide the energy output P. By determining the total radiation incident at the top of the earth's atmosphere, the equivalent temperature of the solar surface is found to be $T = 5784°$K.

This surface temperature is believed to be maintained mostly by radiative processes from the deep-lying regions within the core of the sun that are heated by thermonuclear reactions. Estimates based upon an assumed solar constitution provide a value of 2×10^7 °K for the required temperature of the core region.

The surface layers, called the *photosphere*, are known to consist predominantly of hydrogen. Thus the surface temperature given above leads to the presumption of a low degree of ionization, approximately 0.1 percent. However, at this temperature the electron-electron collisions are predominant, and for the dimensions and times of interest the conductivity is high enough that magnetohydrodynamic effects occur. We should not be surprised to find motions of the solar material to be accompanied by corresponding magnetic field changes, and we shall presently discuss some of these phenomena.

Before doing so it will prove useful to review certain features of the regions beyond the solar surface. Because of the extreme brightness of the photosphere, these upper regions are best examined during an eclipse, although it has proved possible to simulate the effect of an eclipse by inserting an opaque light baffle into a specially constructed solar telescope called a *coronagraph*. Figure 4-1 is a rather schematic sketch of the upper regions of the solar atmosphere, called the corona, as it appears during an eclipse. The corona extends to many times the radius of the sun. The possible existence of a solar dipole magnetic field is often inferred from the form of the

FIG. 4-1   Schematic representation of the corona as observed during an eclipse.

coronal streamers evident in this sketch. The similarity between the shape of the streamers and the pattern of iron filings held near a bar magnet is evident.

On closer examination than is possible to display in this sketch, the lower portions of the solar atmosphere are seen to consist of sprays of solar material that occasionally extend to 15,000 km. These sprays are called *spicules* and tend to give the lower regions the appearance of a grass fire. The region dominated by the spicules is called the *chromosphere*. Extending above the chromosphere and most evident in Fig. 4-1 is the less luminous corona.

Spectroscopic studies have been made to determine the density and temperature of the solar material above the photosphere. Many of the determinations are made by identifying the degree of ionization of such atoms as iron that are present in the chromosphere and corona. Figure 4-2 is a plot showing the electron tem-

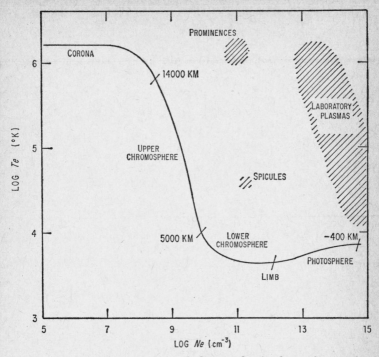

FIG. 4-2   Electron temperature and electron density for various regions above and slightly below the solar surface.

perature T_e and the electron density N_e at various elevations from the solar surface. Elevation marks above and below the solar limb are shown on the plot. We see that the temperature continues to drop slightly beyond the solar surface. But then at larger distances the density continues to drop and the temperature increases, reaching about 10^6 °K at the base of the corona. This observed increase of temperature with distance from the radiating sun has constituted one of the more interesting puzzles of solar physics. Generally, we expect the temperature to decrease with increasing distance from a hot source. Evidently some nonthermodynamic process must work to accomplish this reversed temperature gradient in the solar atmosphere.

Also shown in Fig. 4-2 are the temperatures and densities of the spicules and the prominences. The latter will be discussed later in this chapter. Also shown for comparison are the range of temperatures and densities found in laboratory experiments. We see from the solar densities and temperatures of Fig. 4-2 and from those of Fig. 1-2 that the material of the corona, spicules, and solar surface possess the essential characteristics of a plasma. In general, the solar plasma is less dense than laboratory plasma, but the temperature range available in the laboratory is comparable to that in the solar atmosphere.

Two other spectroscopic observational techniques have contributed unique and essential information about the solar material velocities and magnetic fields. These techniques involve the measurements of Doppler shifts and Zeeman broadening of spectral lines, respectively. These methods have proved valuable not only to solar, but also to other astrophysical work.

In a manner somewhat analogous to the Doppler shifting of the frequency of sound waves due to relative motion of the source and the detector, the frequency of light waves can be displaced. When we deal with light waves, the analysis must proceed on the basis of the special theory of relativity, but the essential aspects are analogous to the sound-wave calculation. Ordinarily, the relativistic effects are overshadowed by the classical shift, which for light of wavelength λ from a source moving at relative velocity v is $\Delta\lambda = \lambda(v/c)$. This Doppler shift provides a ready means for identifying the relative velocity of an astronomical object with respect to the observer. Spectral lines emitted by the object are shifted in wavelength by the amount $\Delta\lambda$. A measurement of the shift together with the wavelength λ of the identical unshifted line from a stationary source yields the relative velocity of the moving object.

Certain spectral lines emitted by elements placed in magnetic fields are split into a number of component lines that are shifted in wavelength from that emitted in the absence of the field. This splitting of the spectral lines is due to an interaction between the magnetic moments of the emitting atoms and the applied magnetic field. This interaction displaces the various atomic energy levels in such a way that transitions between the displaced levels no longer produce light emission at the single wavelengths represented by the unsplit lines. The amount of displacement of the atomic levels is related to the magnitude of the applied magnetic field; in some cases it is directly proportional to the field. When the latter holds, the degree of splitting provides a ready measure of the magnetic field at the emitting region. Sometimes the line splitting is so small that only a line broadening is observed. This line broadening is called Zeeman broadening.

With these observational techniques in mind, we return to a discussion of the solar photosphere. An examination of the solar surface reveals a number of remarkable features. One of these features is seen as dark spots on the disc. These are called sun spots and may be of the order of 10 000 km or more across. Since these spots persist for a very long time, they may be used to follow the solar rotation. The average rotational period is observed to be about 27 days. However, there is considerable differential rotation; the period at the equator is 25 days and at 60 degrees latitude about 29 days.

Since the spots appear darker than the surrounding photosphere, they are cooler than their surroundings. They often appear in groups, particularly pairs. Spectroscopic measurements of the Zeeman broadening of spectral lines reveal the presence of strong magnetic fields in sun spots. Fields of 2000 gauss are observed in large spots. Generally, the polarity of the field is opposite in the two members of a pair, the magnetic lines leaving the surface in one spot and returning at the other. The pairs in one hemisphere tend to be oriented magnetically so that all "leading" spots, in the direction of rotation, have the same polarity. And in the opposite hemisphere the polarities of the "leading" spots are reversed.

The spots are observed to follow a somewhat irregular cycle of occurrence, reaching a maximum number each 11 years. They begin to appear at latitudes near 30 degrees, then increase in numbers at lower and lower latitudes until their frequency of occurrence drops off again at the close of the cycle. In each succeeding 11-year cycle the magnetic polarity of "leading" spots in each hemisphere is observed to reverse. The return to similar magnetic polarity therefore occurs on a 22-year cycle.

The fact that the sun rotates and is an electrically conducting fluid leads to the expectation that the sun may have an over-all magnetic field. This expectation is certainly in keeping with the presently accepted supposition that the earth's dipole field results from a self-exciting dynamo action of the earth's conducting-fluid core. Again making use of the magnetic Zeeman broadening of spectral lines, an over-all solar dipole field has been detected; this result supports the earlier interpretation of the coronal streamers.

The magnitude of the dipole field is variable, but is of the order of a few gauss at the poles. The polarity of the dipole field was observed to reverse in 1957–1958 during the maximum of the last 11-year sun spot cycle. If the dipole field returns to the former polarity during the present cycle, a close correlation between the dipole field and the sun spots will have been established.

A possible connection between the two has been suggested by Babcock. He supposes that, because of the high conductivity of the solar material, the magnetic field lines associated with the dipole field cannot penetrate deeply and are constrained to lie near the surface. The differential solar rotation is supposed to wind up the field lines, as shown in Fig. 4-3a. The effect of this winding is to

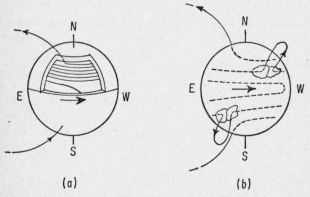

FIG. 4-3 (a) The winding up of the surface-confined solar dipole field by differential rotation. (b) The production of bipolar magnetic regions by expulsion of field lines from the solar surface. (From Babcock, Astrophysical Journal, Vol. 133, p. 572, 1961)

increase the number of field lines per area, that is, to increase the magnetic field intensity. Babcock argues that the field is thereby sufficiently increased so that the lines and the material tied to them possess sufficiently high total pressure $(p + B^2/8\pi)$ that they are forced out of the solar surface, forming bipolar magnetic regions or spots like those shown in Fig. 4-3b. By a complex sequence of hydromagnetic arguments Babcock supports his belief that the spot fields eventually reverse the over-all dipole field during each half of the 22-year cycle. Although it is not clear that the Babcock formulation is correct, a connection between the dipole and spot magnetic field actions seems quite likely.

An examination of the solar surface with much greater resolving power than that required to study the sun spots reveals smaller-scale markings called *granulations*, which give the sun a superficial appearance not unlike that of an orange. The individual granulations appear and disappear within minutes and are of the order of 1000 km in size. Because of their small size, the most satisfactory observations are made at the top of the earth's atmosphere by balloon-borne telescopes. Except in scale, the appearance is like the convective turbulent motions in a heated pot of viscous fluid. Spectroscopic examination designed to measure the material velocities in the granulations by Doppler shifts shows these granulations to be convection cells. Hot solar material rises to the surface, cools, then falls again to lower levels along the edges of the cells. Thus a most important mode by which energy is transmitted to the solar surface must be via this turbulent layer of convection cells. Indeed, the lower temperature of the dark sun spots may be understood as the action of the spot magnetic fields in slowing the convective processes by which heat is transferred to the surface. The fields are probably strong enough to inhibit the turbulence, since the magnetic pressure $B^2/8\pi$ is approximately equal to the gas pressure of 10^5 dynes/cm^2.

The granulation turbulence seen in the photosphere has suggested a possible mechanism whereby the chromosphere and corona might be heated to the high temperatures observed. If sound waves were generated by the granulation turbulence and if these waves could propagate into the chromosphere, the decreasing density there should cause the waves to become supersonic and shocks should develop in a manner akin to that discussed in § 2-4. These shock waves could then dissipate their energy in the corona, thereby supplying the required heating. Estimates of the sound-wave en-

ergies generated in the convection zone are found to be adequate
to balance the observed losses from the solar atmosphere.

However, such a process will not work. The temperature minimum close to the solar surface, noted earlier, produces a minimum in the sound velocity. Thus waves incident from a wide
range of angles upon this velocity minimum will suffer refractions
that will bend the waves back into regions of higher velocity and
toward the solar surface. Thus although adequate energy may be
available in the turbulence to heat the atmosphere, sound waves
cannot penetrate the temperature minimum to do the heating.
Nevertheless, the reflection of acoustical energy by this minimum
has provided insight into an interesting set of observations of the
photosphere.

As indicated above, Doppler shift measurements have been made
over substantial areas of the sun to determine the material velocities in the photosphere. If these measurements are made as a
function of time, it is found that the material motions tend to re-
produce themselves with a five-minute period. That is, the photospheric material oscillates. However, at a particular region the
oscillation goes through only a few cycles, then ceases for a rather
long time. Now the propagation time for a sound wave from the
surface to the temperature minimum and return is calculated to be
5 minutes! Thus the oscillation of the photospheric plasma seems
to be supported by the reflected acoustic waves, although pure
acoustic waves do not account for all details of the motion.

The spicules, which extend over the entire solar surface, may
provide an alternate pathway for propagation of energy from the
convection layer to the corona. The depth to which the spicules
penetrate the photosphere is not known. However, if they were to
extend to the convection zone, an efficient path for energy transfer
might be provided. This possibility is reinforced by Zeeman broadening measurements that indicate magnetic fields of 10 gauss or so
directed along the spicules. Thus waves generated by the photospheric oscillations and turbulence could conceivably propagate as
hydromagnetic waves along the spicules to the upper chromosphere
and lower corona.

The manner in which hydromagnetic waves transport and deposit
the requisite energy from a turbulent, wave-generating region to

the corona is not known, but it may proceed as follows. The convective layer may generate pressure waves that are essentially acoustic waves in the photosphere. As these waves propagate outwards, they may evolve into shock waves and hydromagnetic waves. The acoustic shock waves should dissipate most of their energy in the lower chromosphere, but the hydromagnetic waves may propagate into the upper chromosphere and corona. If the generated hydromagnetic wave amplitudes are comparable to the steady magnetic field in which they propagate, the compressibility of the plasma will cause the wave velocity given by Eq. 2-28 to be modified to that given by Eq. 2-50:

$$c_p{}^2 = [B_0{}^2 + b(t)^2]/4\pi\rho, \qquad (4\text{-}2)$$

where B_0 is the steady magnetic field, b is the wave magnetic field, and ρ is the plasma density. For $b \approx B_0$ the larger amplitude portions of the wave have higher velocity than the smaller and tend to overtake the smaller. The waves are thus steepened, possibly into shock waves which can dissipate the amounts of energy required to heat the corona. The wave steepening is further aided by the continual decrease of density with distance from the photosphere. Attenuation calculations similar to those discussed in § 2-3 show that such propagation could be effective for carrying the required energy. Nevertheless, no such propagations have been observed in the spicules or elsewhere. The problem of coronal heating is still an open question.

Associated with the dark, cool sun spots are brighter regions, called *faculae*. The faculae appear in an area before the appearance of the spot and outlast the spot by as much as several solar rotations. Faculae are easily visible over the entire disc in the light of the H_α hydrogen line. The faculae show a granulated structure much like that of the background photosphere, but these granule lifetimes are longer, of the order of one hour. Spectral measurements show the lower regions of faculae to be cooler and the upper regions hotter than the surrounding photosphere. That the faculae are an integral and important aspect of sun spots is evident by their earlier appearance and later disappearance. However, very little is known about the details of the interdependence of the two features.

Also closely associated with sun spot areas are the short-lived sudden increases of light intensity known as *flares*. In times of high numbers of sun spots, flares may occur with a frequency approaching one per hour and may last for times ranging from a few minutes to a few hours. The increase to maximum light intensity occurs in a very few minutes. Radio frequency radiations are also produced by solar flares; the intensity fluctuation approximately parallels that of the light, but is thought to be much more closely associated with the ejection of particles than is the light.

The radio frequency emissions associated with flares have very interesting time histories. A particularly instructive relationship is shown in Fig. 4-4. Here the time variation of the radio frequency

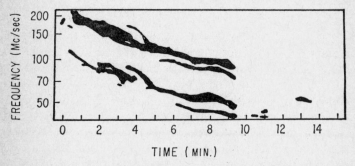

FIG. 4-4 Frequencies of the maximum intensity of radio waves emitted in a solar flare as a function of time. (Reprinted from *The Sun* edited by P. Kuiper by permission of the University of Chicago Press. Copyright 1953 by The University of Chicago.)

spectrum is shown. The black streaks indicate the general trend of the most intense components. We notice that at any particular time there are two components differing in frequency by a factor of two, and that the two bands are very similar in structural details. These effects suggest that the emission at all frequencies is due to one phenomenon and that one band is simply the second harmonic of the other. Large-amplitude electron oscillations at the plasma frequency can be excited in a plasma and can possess nonlinear effects such that not only the fundamental, but higher harmonics as well, are radiated by the oscillations.

A connection between the changing emission frequency and the location of the disturbance is suggested by Fig. 4-2, which indicates the rather strong decrease of electron density with distance above the solar surface. This decrease of electron density implies a comparable decrease in plasma frequency. Thus the progress of the intensity maxima from higher to lower frequency with time as seen in Fig. 4-4 strongly suggests the motion of the generating disturbance from lower to higher levels of the solar atmosphere. Since the electron density distribution is known, the apparent speed of the disturbance can be calculated if we assume that the signal comes from the region where its frequency equals the local plasma frequency. The speeds so calculated are of the order of those seen in the simultaneously ejected streams of corpuscular material.

When a flare occurs at the solar limb, the progress of the ejected material can be followed. Velocities of 1000 km/sec are often observed to heights of 10^5 km. The ejection of plasma material from the vicinity of sun spots implies that substantial magnetic fields may be carried along with the material. In § 4-2 the injection of this plasma into the interplanetary space will be seen to provide the most powerful perturbing influence upon that region. The mechanism whereby the neighborhood of a spot, namely, the faculae regions, impart the 10^{28}–10^{29} ergs contained in a typical flare is not known.

The last solar feature that we discuss is also related spatially, hence probably physically, to the spot regions. These structures are called *prominences* when seen on the limb during an eclipse or by use of the coronagraph. They are called *filaments* when seen on the disc. On the limb they appear bright against the dark background; on the disc they are dark against the photosphere. The structures have the form of a sheet that may be as large as 200 000 km along the solar surface, extend 100 000 km above the surface and be 5 000 km thick. The proximity of prominences to sun spot regions, their sheet-like form and their shapes, of which Fig. 4-5 is a characteristic example, suggest the strong influence of magnetic fields.

Prominence or filament development may occur over a period of many days, and a prominence may persist for tens of days. However, motions on a much shorter time scale are evident on the limb, where significant changes in height and structure may take place during a one-hour interval.

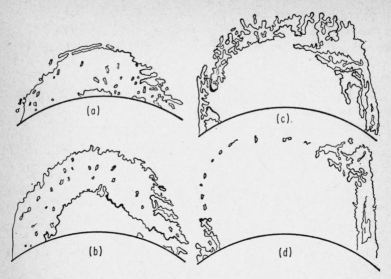

FIG. 4-5 Sketch of a rising solar prominence. Elapsed time between frames for such a prominence is of the order of 0.5 hour. (Reprinted from *The Sun* edited by P. Kuiper by permission of The University of Chicago Press. Copyright 1953 by The University of Chicago.)

The density of a prominence is, from Fig. 4-2, about 100 times that of the surrounding corona, and its temperature about 1/200. Thus the pressures inside and outside the prominence will be roughly comparable. However, the lower prominence temperature should serve to "condense" neighboring coronal plasma into the structure by degrading its energy and increasing its interaction probability with the cooler prominence material. That this process probably takes place is supported by the dark, hence lower density, coronal layer in the space around a prominence and by the predominantly descending mass motions observed in prominences. Thus the cool prominence is thought to "condense" and drain away a portion of the neighboring coronal plasma.

In all of these workings near and above the solar surface we see the interplay of the conducting plasma with magnetic fields. In most cases the complexity of the interactions is sufficient to have prevented much more than speculative explanations. However, in spite of the difficulties involved, increasingly more detailed observational data are becoming available, and applications of the principles discussed in earlier chapters are expected to provide viable explanations of the phenomena discussed here.

§ 4-2   The Solar Wind.   We next discuss the interplanetary effects of the more or less steady state aspects of the sun. The absence of regions of great activity, such as spots and flares, will be assumed, and the consequences of the temperature and density distributions in the steady state corona will be examined.

Comets that traverse the interplanetary space have proved to be a useful probe for examining the properties of that space. Comets have a head and tail consisting of material derived from a solid, invisible nucleus that is located within the head. The comet is formed of the material ablated from the nucleus as it interacts with the solar plasma and radiation. In the so-called type 1 comets, the tails are straight and pointed almost directly away from the sun. This result can only hold if the acceleration of the tail material away from the sun considerably exceeds the solar gravitational acceleration at the comet. For type 2 and type 3 comets, which have curved tails, it seems likely that the much lower accelerations of their tail material can be supplied in large part by solar light pressure. However, for straight-tailed comets this acceleration source is entirely inadequate. On the other hand, a rather modest steady streaming of particles from the sun throughout the interplanetary space could press the type 1 tails into the observed orientation. These comet observations constituted the first evidence for the streaming of solar material into interplanetary space.

The density of the streaming material is generally thought to be of the order of 10 particles/cm^3. Its temperature may be from 10^4–10^6 °K. The Debye distance from Eq. 1-1 is then $D = 6.90(T/n_e)^{1/2}$ cm $\approx$ 2 km at most. This distance is small compared to others of importance in the space involved. A Debye sphere would contain about 3×10^{11} particles; thus the behavior of this very tenuous medium is also plasma-like.

Direct confirmation of the existence of the steady "solar wind" is not trivial, because the wind cannot be observed near the earth's surface. Since the wind material is a highly electrically conducting plasma, it will be shunted around the neighborhood of the earth by the earth's magnetic field. Actually, there are indirect means whereby the presence of the solar wind can be inferred at the earth's surface. These evidences involve an interpretation of perturbations upon the steady-state wind; these effects are discussed in § 4-3.

Thus a direct observation, planned to detect the solar wind, must be carried out at a location sufficiently removed from the earth that the terrestrial magnetic field is of negligible importance. Just such measurements were made using the Explorer 10 and Mariner II space probes. An ion detector capable of determining the energy spectrum of solar protons in the streaming plasma was mounted on the Mariner II space craft in such a way that it was always directed at the sun and perpendicular to the space craft's velocity, which was some tens of kilometers per second.

Figure 4-6 shows the arrangement of this analyzer. Plasma from the solar direction was admitted into the entrance as shown. The plasma ions and electrons were directed between the parallel, curved plates of the analyzer, where an applied electric field E acted upon those particles of mass m and charge q so that they followed a mean radius R given by

$$mv^2/R = Eq. \qquad (4\text{-}3)$$

Here v is the particle velocity. It is clear that the choice of the direction of E as shown in Fig. 4-6 will cause positively charged ions to curve in the direction of the parallel plates; electrons will be deflected oppositely and be lost as they impinge on the outer plate.

We may rewrite Eq. 4-3 in the form

$$mv^2/2q = W/q = ER/2, \qquad (4\text{-}4)$$

where $W = mv^2/2$ is the particle kinetic energy. Thus an appropriate choice of E will cause ions of a given W/q ratio to follow the mean radius and leave the plates at the exit aperture. Since most of the ions are expected to be protons, as is the solar corona, q is the proton charge, and the device is seen to perform an energy

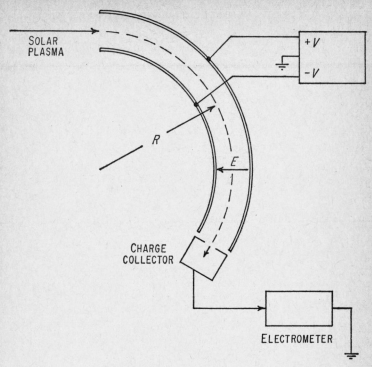

FIG. 4-6 Ion energy analyzer used on Mariner II to measure the solar wind velocity, density, and ion temperature.

analysis of the protons. The current produced by the ions collected beyond the exit aperture is measured by use of the electrometer shown.

During the observation period, while the space craft was outside the influence of the geomagnetic field, the electric field E was varied in steps so that ions of various W/q values were detected in turn. The electrometer currents for the selected W/q values were then telemetered to ground stations and used to construct energy spectra of the solar plasma ions.

Figure 4-7 shows two samples of the spectra obtained at different times during the flight. Increasing channel numbers correspond approximately to 50 percent energy increases from one channel to the next. The two spectra are quite different, showing that considerable variation occurs with time. The spectrum in Fig. 4-7a appeared to represent the steady state plasma flow. The maximum occurred in channel two corresponding to a mean proton

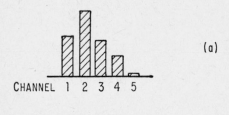

(a)

CHANNEL 1 2 3 4 5

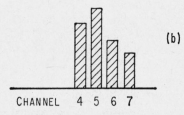

(b)

CHANNEL   4 5 6 7

FIG. 4-7   A selected sample of ion energy spectra measured by the Mariner II analyzer shown in Fig. 4-6.   (a) Quiet solar wind conditions. (b) Perturbed solar wind conditions.

velocity of about $v = 460$ km/sec. The integral under the spectrum is representative of the ion density, and that given in Fig. 4-7a corresponds to about $n = 2.5$ protons/cm^3. The width of the maximum gives a measure of the random velocities of the plasma ions in the direction in which the detector pointed. Although it is obviously difficult to make a width determination from channel spacings as coarse as those used, an approximate temperature of $T = 2 \times 10^5$ °K results from Fig. 4-7a when it is assumed that all thermal motions occur in the direction of the bulk plasma velocity.

During the times of solar disturbance represented by the spectrum of Fig. 4-7b the plasma characteristics were approximately: velocity $v = 810$ km/sec, density $n = 4.5$ protons/cm^3, temperature $T = 7.4 \times 10^5$ °K. Roughly, the velocity and density are double and the temperature triple the steady state values.

Thus the Mariner II observations establish the existence of a solar wind and yield approximate quantitative measurements of its properties. At present we focus our attention upon the steady state wind represented by Fig. 4-7a. In § 4-3 the discussion of the perturbed conditions will be continued.

From the velocity, temperature, and density given above, the plasma flux nv is calculated to be 1.2×10^8 cm^{-2} sec^{-1} and the plasma energy density $n(\frac{1}{2}mv^2 + \frac{1}{2}kT) \approx \frac{1}{2}nmv^2 \approx 4.4 \times 10^{-9}$ ergs/cm^3. The Alfvén velocity in this plasma, for a reasonable assumption of 5×10^{-5} gauss for the interplanetary magnetic field, is from Eq. 2-28, $V_A = B/(4\pi M_i n) = 69$ km/sec. Thus the ratio of plasma velocity to Alfvén velocity is $v/V_A = 6.7$, and it is expected that a hydromagnetic shock may develop in the vicinity of the earth. Such a shock has recently been observed. The magnetic energy for the above field is $B^2/8\pi = 1 \times 10^{-10}$ erg/cm^3. Since the magnetic energy is small compared to the plasma flow energy, the magnetic fields are swept along by the plasma flow. In the absence of any rotational forces the flow and the solar magnetic field should be radial. However, the solar rotation introduces a spiraling of the flow and the field lines.

Before the Mariner II and Explorer 10 observations there existed strong theoretical reasons for a considerable degree of certainty about the steady solar wind that presumably affects the comet tails. The pertinent arguments, developed originally by Chapman and by Parker, pertain to the behavior of the coronal plasma. Chapman's model is concerned with a static coronal plasma. Although this simplified model provides for no solar plasma flow, it gives considerable insight on the conditions to be expected near the earth.

According to Chapman's static, spherically symmetric model, the temperature and density distribution of the solar atmosphere should be determined by the heat flow within the atmosphere and the gravitational forces acting upon it. The heat flow H from material at temperature T a distance r from the center of the sun is given by

$$H = -4\pi r^2 Q \frac{dT}{dr}. \qquad (4\text{-}5)$$

Here Q is the thermal conductivity of the coronal plasma. Neglecting radiative losses, H is a constant independent of r. For a plasma,

$Q \propto T^{5/2}$. Assuming that Q is independent of density, Eq. 4-5 can be integrated to yield

$$T(r) = T(r_0)\left(\frac{r_0}{r}\right)^{2/7}, \qquad (4\text{-}6)$$

where the constant of integration is obtained by setting $T(r_0)$ equal to the known temperature at some radial distance r_0. Setting $T(r_0 = 1.06R_\odot) = 10^6\,°K$, the temperature of the solar corona at the earth's orbit is expected to be about $2 \times 10^5\,°K$, in agreement with the Mariner II result. $R_\odot$ stands for the solar radius.

The temperature distribution of Eq. 4-6 can be used to calculate the density if we assume that the radial pressure gradient dp/dr equals the gravitational attraction. Thus

$$\frac{dp}{dr} = \frac{-GM_\odot m_i n}{r^2}, \qquad (4\text{-}7)$$

where G is the gravitational constant, $M_\odot$ is the solar mass, m_i is the ion mass, and n is the coronal ion number density. Then for an ideal gas Eqs. 4-6 and 4-7 yield, on integration of the latter, a rather complicated expression for the radial dependence of the number density:

$$n(r) = n(r_0)\left(\frac{r}{r_0}\right)^{2/7} \exp\left\{-\frac{7GM_\odot m_i}{10kTr_0}\left[1 - \left(\frac{r_0}{r}\right)^{5/7}\right]\right\}. \qquad (4\text{-}8)$$

Taking $n(r_0 = 1.06R_\odot) = 1.4 \times 10^8$, Eq. 4-8 gives $n \approx 300$ ions/cm³ at the earth's orbit. The temperature dependence is very strong; if $T(r_0) = 0.9 \times 10^6\,°K$, n at the earth's orbit is reduced to about 75 ions/cm³. Thus on this static model the earth is expected to be immersed in a rather hot plasma of appreciable density.

The static model is not adequate because plasma at the coronal temperature is observed to extend so far out from the surface that the solar gravitational field cannot prohibit its escape from the sun. Beyond a few solar radii the outer parts of the coronal plasma are thus expected to be expanding outward into space with substantial velocity.

The action of the gravitational field is crucial to this high-velocity streaming. If there were no gravity, the outer corona would simply evaporate into the surrounding space. However, the gravitational field has a compressing and filtering effect, allowing only those ions acquiring radially directed velocities in excess of that required to overcome the gravity field to escape. The effect is similar to the expansion of gas through a nozzle into a near vacuum, the large directed velocity deriving from the thermal energy of the contained gas. Just as in a nozzle, the coronal expansion in the gravitational field becomes supersonic on escape. To assure the flow of a steady solar wind, the energy extracted from the plasma in directed motion must be replaced. A high thermal conductivity of the corona would permit the required energy interchange. In the lower corona, estimates of the temperature gradient are as low as 3°K per km; such low gradients almost certainly indicate the high thermal conductivities required in the coronal plasma.

If the coronal plasma temperature is for any reason locally raised to greater than about 3×10^6 °K, the gravitational field cannot hold the bulk of the plasma. It is then expected to expand explosively. Such local heating may occur over regions that produce solar flares; we return to this point in § 4-3.

In its progress through interplanetary space the solar wind interacts with magnetic fields that may be associated with any of the planets. Besides the earth it is reasonably certain that Jupiter has a substantial field. The extent of these and any other planetary fields is not sufficient to affect in any substantial way the over-all pattern of the plasma flow. However, the flow and the fields interact very strongly in the vicinity of the planet. Because of the relative abundance of available data, we limit this discussion primarily to the interaction with the geomagnetic field.

A streaming plasma interacting with a dipole magnetic field exerts a pressure upon the field. In a general way we see that the plasma will press against the field and compress it until the magnetic pressure equals the plasma pressure. The effect upon the geomagnetic dipole field pictured undistorted in Fig. 4-8a is to press it into a shape like that shown in Fig. 4-8b. The wind will also pass around the earth at a distance approximately prescribed by the equality of magnetic and plasma pressure. Later, on the down-wind side of the earth, thermal motions of the wind may cause the stream to close as shown. Thus the earth is left by the steady solar wind in a cavity "carved out" by the dipole magnetic field. This cavity is called the magnetosphere. Detailed calcula-

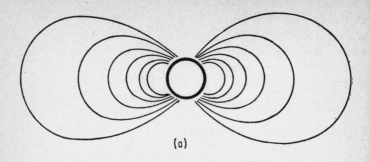

(a)

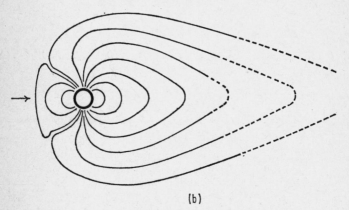

(b)

FIG. 4-8 (a) The geomagnetic field as it would appear if there were no solar wind. (b) The field as it is distorted by the solar wind. Since there is considerable doubt about the precise shape of the down-wind portions, they are shown dashed.

tions of the shape of the cavity are very difficult, and none of the proposed solutions will be presented here. One result of these calculations is that the boundary of the cavity on the side toward the sun is expected to lie at a distance of 5 to 10 earth radii.

The plasma characteristics determined from the Mariner II measurements showed the plasma velocity to exceed the Alfvén velocity in interplanetary space. This condition will hold just outside the magnetosphere, where the magnetic field is essentially that of interplanetary space. Thus the solar plasma on reaching the plasma-magnetosphere interface will tend to pile up and stream around the sides of the cavity at supersonic velocities. These high flow velocities are expected to lead to hydromagnetic turbulence near the interface.

Measurements of the geomagnetic field have been made using a variety of space probes. One of these measurements is the location by Explorer 12 of the magnetic field boundary on the side toward the sun. During quiet solar conditions the boundary was detected at about 10 earth radii. Inside the boundary, the magnetic field was generally observed to be steady. Abruptly as the probe moved outward across the boundary region the fields became highly variable with particularly sudden changes in direction. Several passes across the boundary region yielded similar results. The conclusion is evident that these abrupt changes in the character of the magnetic field signal the increase of hydromagnetic turbulence at the boundary.

Thus it seems clear that the characteristics of the solar corona and the solar gravitational field produce a steady solar wind that penetrates at least to the earth's orbit, where an interaction with the geomagnetic field occurs. In the next sections we consider the perturbations that may be superimposed upon this steady plasma flow by transient solar conditions, and the effects of these perturbations upon the geomagnetic field and upon the upper atmosphere.

§ 4-3 **Perturbations of the Steady Wind.** The solar surface and solar atmosphere are seldom quiet. Various magnetic field and plasma flow perturbations occur; some of the observational details of these events were cited in the discussion of sun spots, flares, etc. In particular, a solar flare, possibly generated by abnormal local heating in sun spot regions, may expand explosively from the sun. The material ejected should be hotter and travel at greater speed than the steady wind, thus producing a perturbation upon it. A wide variety of evidence for the manner in which these disturbances are propagated to the vicinity of the earth is available. Some of these disturbances will be discussed here, along with the manner in which they contribute to the actual state of the perturbed solar wind.

Possibly the most primitive observation relating solar conditions to the terrestrial atmosphere is the long-established correlation between sun spot activity and auroral occurrence. Roughly coincident 11-year cycles are observed for each. The intimate nature of the sun-earth link is shown, in this case, by the occurrence of enhanced auroral activity some 30 hours following strong solar flares.

For a more detailed view of the interaction of the perturbed solar wind with the terrestrial environment it is useful to consider the strong variations of the geomagnetic field that are called *magnetic storms*. We have seen from the discussion of Fig. 4-8 that the steady solar wind produces distortions of the field. We expect any perturbations of the solar wind to be reflected by disturbances of the field. Further, since the amplitudes and directions of these field changes can be measured, the changes should in principle at least be interpretable in terms of some model for the interaction of the perturbed wind with the field.

From Fig. 4-8 it is easy to suppose that solar wind perturbations of the field should be easily observed near the equator. Any variation in the compression of the component of the field parallel to the earth's surface by the wind should be most evident there. This so-called horizontal component of the field at the equator is about 0.3 gauss, and it is against this background field that changes must be measured.

We now describe the sequence of equatorial horizontal-component magnetic field changes constituting a typical magnetic storm. Some 30 hours after visual or radio emission allows identification of a solar flare, the horizontal field component rapidly increases. The delay time evidently corresponds to that required for the transport of the flare material from the sun to the earth. The magnetic field increase is called a *sudden commencement* and is the first and principal event of the initial phase of the storm. During this phase the field may increase by some 2×10^{-4} gauss within a period of several minutes. The initial phase is followed by a decrease that may continue for several hours. During this second phase the field becomes less than the original unperturbed value by an amount greater than the sudden commencement maximum. This second, *main phase*, decays over a period of many days to the steady value. Although sudden commencements are observed almost simultaneously all over the earth, larger amplitude field changes occur on the sunlit side, where the bulk of the solar plasma impinges upon the magnetosphere.

Some of the characteristics of the disturbed solar plasma that cause the magnetic storms were obtained from the Mariner II plasma observations discussed in § 4-2. Disturbed conditions led to a doubling of the plasma wind velocity and density and a tripling of the temperature. For either the steady state or the perturbed solar wind conditions, the plasma conductivity is sufficiently high to limit severely the penetration into the plasma of the geomagnetic field.

Thus the plasma burst of higher density and bulk velocity that is superimposed upon the steady wind should further distort the geomagnetic field, and the horizontal component at the equator should increase. The plasma velocity and density measured by Mariner II during solar disturbances are appropriate to account for the observed 10^{-4} gauss amplitudes of sudden commencements. Thus the magnetic field aspects of sudden commencements seem reasonably well understood.

Explorer 12 measurements have also shown the shift in the boundary of the magnetosphere caused by solar disturbances. Whereas the boundaries detected for quiet times occur at about 10 earth radii on the sun side, during very moderate disturbances the boundary was shifted to about 8 to 9 earth radii.

No satisfactory account of the magnetic storm main phase has yet been given. This phase has often been attributed to a current that is supposed to circle the earth in a westward direction, thus reducing the steady dipole field. The stability of such a ring current is supposed to account for the long duration of the main phase. However, no one has been able to show conclusively that such a ring current must flow as a natural consequence of the plasma-dipole field interaction. Chapman and Ferraro first proposed an idealized model to account for the sudden commencement. In their model an infinite plasma impinged upon a magnetic dipole field. They suggested that a ring current might arise as a result of a polarization field which they found would form on the sides of the plasma cavity. But no proof of this supposition has been given. Various more elaborate interaction models have been developed, but none satisfactorily accounts for the main phase.

Figure 4-8b shows that the pressure of the solar plasma distorts the geomagnetic field in such a way that plasma may penetrate much closer to the earth at a certain latitude. The geometry of the geomagnetic field and the Mariner II plasma measurements can be combined to yield a latitude corresponding to the depression shown in Fig. 4-8b. This calculated latitude is approximately 68°, in close agreement with the latitude of maximum observed auroral activity. The increased plasma pressures during magnetic storms could make regions in the upper atmosphere at those latitudes accessible to the solar plasma. Thus energetic solar particles could penetrate the upper atmosphere, ionize atmospheric atoms, and produce auroras. Doppler-shifted hydrogen lines seen in auroras support the view that some high-energy solar protons of 3000 km/sec velocity do enter the atmosphere, but they probably cannot penetrate to auroral heights. Thus auroral excitation may be largely due to the plasma electrons.

We have seen that a plasma burst ejected from the sun as part of a solar flare propagates to the earth and produces magnetic storms and auroras on interacting with the geomagnetic field and the atmosphere. Details of the progress of the plasma burst from the sun to the earth must be inferred from other observations. Cosmic rays, which can be detected on the earth and in space probes, have given particularly valuable information concerning these interplanetary regions. Since the cosmic ray particles are predominantly protons, their interaction with the magnetic fields that may be carried by the solar bursts affect their trajectories and hence the rate at which they arrive at the earth.

To appreciate how cosmic rays can be used to measure interplanetary conditions, we need to review briefly the origins of these particles. The primary cosmic ray protons incident upon the top of the earth's atmosphere may be divided into those of solar and those of nonsolar origin. The solar protons, generated by the actions of solar flares, possess energies ranging from a fraction of 10^6 eV to several times 10^9 eV. These cosmic ray protons are not to be confused with the much lower energy (1000 km/sec $\approx 4 \times 10^4$ eV) protons that make up the plasma ejected in a flare. The production of the high-energy solar protons is called a high-energy solar particle event. These events are relatively few in number, but are detected during periods of great flare activity.

The cosmic rays of nonsolar origin are generated elsewhere in the galaxy and probably beyond the confines of the galaxy by processes that are not well understood. Possible acceleration mechanisms of these cosmic rays have been proposed. It is sufficient to note here that the galactic and extragalactic cosmic rays have energies largely unattainable by known solar processes. The spectrum of these nonsolar particles extends at least to 10^{20} eV.

Both the solar and nonsolar cosmic rays are capable of generating cascades of secondary particles as they interact with the earth's atmosphere. However, only for a primary particle energy roughly in excess of 450×10^6 eV are sufficiently energetic secondaries produced to allow members of the cascade to reach ground level. Thus all ground-based cosmic ray measurements are insensitive to primary particles below this energy.

The type of secondaries produced by the primary interaction with an atmospheric atom depends upon the primary energy. For proton energies in excess of 10^{10} or 10^{11} eV, the incoming proton produces mesons and nucleons that further interact with the nuclei at lower levels, producing more secondaries. Pi mesons are among the secondaries, and these mesons decay rapidly into mu mesons. The mu mesons are very penetrating. Most of the mu mesons and many nucleons from the cascade reach the ground. Thus nucleons and mu mesons can be detected from events of these energies.

Below about 10^{10} eV primary energy, few mesons are produced in the cascade. Hence these events of lower energy are detected at ground level primarily by counters sensitive to the nucleon component; neutron counters are used for this detection work. Thus it is seen that the meson detectors are largely sensitive to the highest energy, hence nonsolar, cosmic rays, whereas the neutron detectors are sensitive to both solar and nonsolar particles.

Using meson detectors, Forbush observed decreases of a few percent in the nonsolar cosmic ray flux to be closely correlated with the main phase of magnetic storms. Figure 4-9 shows the cosmic ray records from three detectors along with the magnetic

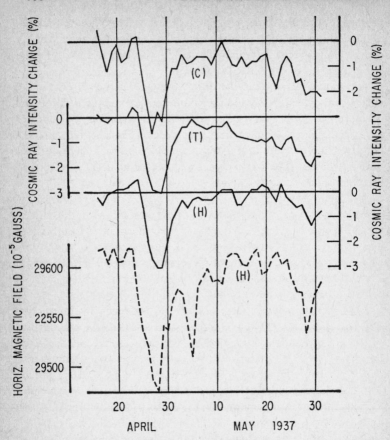

FIG. 4-9 Correlated records of the Forbush decrease and the magnetic storm of April 25–30, 1937. Cosmic ray intensity changes are shown for three stations: Cheltenham, United States (C); Teolayucan, Mexico (T); Huancayo, Peru (H). Horizontal magnetic field intensity is shown at Huancayo, Peru. (From Forbush, Proc. National Academy of Sciences, Vol. 44, p. 28, 1957)

record from an equatorial magnetometer in Huancayo, Peru, for the storm of April 25–30, 1937. The inference usually drawn from observations such as these is that some property of the solar plasma burst responsible for the distortion of the geomagnetic field prohibits the galactic cosmic ray flux from reaching the earth. Since the cosmic rays are electrically charged, it is generally assumed that magnetic and/or electric fields within the plasma are responsible.

Various theories have been proposed to describe the field configurations required to accomplish the observed Forbush decreases. Each of these theories involves the dynamics of solar flare production and propagation, for only an analysis of these processes will lead to a description of the fields in the vicinity of the earth. Parker has proposed that the burst of plasma sent out by flares is capable of radially compressing the spiraling interplanetary magnetic field lines near the earth. The resulting field intensification, shown geometrically in Fig. 4-10a, could then prohibit the lowest-energy galactic cosmic rays from reaching the earth by shortening their radii of curvature. Several other researchers have proposed that the plasma material ejected in a flare actually stretches out magnetic field lines from the sun, forming a magnetic bottle like that shown in Fig. 4-10b. The bottle could then deflect galactic cosmic rays away from the earth while it encloses the earth. It is not yet clear whether either of these models or any others presently proposed represents what actually happens. However, some additional insight on this question is available from studies of the high-energy cosmic rays of solar origin.

High-energy solar particle events can be very complex. The manner in which a group of particles reaches the earth from the sun depends critically upon the particle energy and upon the conditions of the intervening plasma. These conditions, in turn, depend upon the preceding sequence of solar flare activity. Thus each high-energy solar particle event requires a separate analysis that takes into account not only the details of the particle's arrival at the earth, but also the previous solar activity as reflected by the conditions of the interplanetary plasma.

From the start of the present solar cycle in 1954 through 1961, 10 high-energy solar particle events were recorded. Each event is detected by a rapid increase in the neutron arrival rate to several times the original value within about 10 minutes, followed by a subsequent decay to the original value in about one hour. In order to show the type of analysis required to interpret such an event, a particular one that occurred on May 4, 1960, will be described.

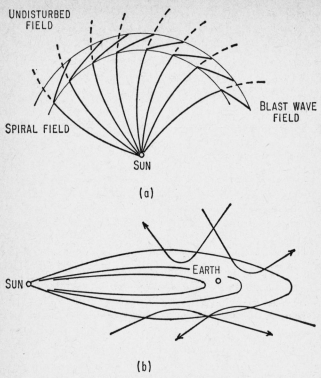

FIG. 4-10 **(a)** Solar flare blast wave compression of interplanetary field. The solid lines show the effect of the blast wave, and the dashed lines are extensions of the undisturbed spiral field. **(b)** Flare-produced magnetic bottle deflecting cosmic rays from the earth.

Two Forbush decreases of the galactic cosmic rays occurred in the days immediately before May 4. The later of these was detected on April 29. Thus by May 4 that flare's effects had proceeded well beyond the earth's orbit, perhaps leaving the magnetic fields between sun and earth in a rather uncomplicated spiral condition. The direction of the spiraled magnetic field at the earth possibly made an angle of about 50 deg with respect to the earth-sun line. From this field configuration it is seen that particles should be able to move from sun to earth rather simply by following the spiral form of the field.

On May 4 at 1000 Universal Time (UT), more commonly known as Greenwich time, the start of a large solar flare was detected visually in the area of the west limb that had ejected the earlier Forbush-decrease producing flares. This new large flare generated microwave noise that began to reach a maximum intensity at the earth at 1015 UT. Since this noise is generated by the same process that ejects the high-energy particles, the particles left the sun at 1007 UT, the eight-minute electromagnetic wave transit time being subtracted from 1015 UT. The particles were detected at the earth at 1029 UT, 14 minutes after the microwave noise. Thus the particle transit time was $14 + 8 = 22$ minutes.

As such particles arrive at the earth, their trajectories are influenced by the geomagnetic field. Particles aimed at the equatorial regions must pass through more extensive magnetic fields perpendicular to their trajectory than do those aimed at the polar regions. In this way the geomagnetic field performs an energy analysis of the incoming particles. Thus the intensity increase at various latitudes can be used as a measure of the particle energies. In the May 4 event the neutron increase was detected at such latitudes as to indicate the presence of particles with energies greater than 1.8×10^9 eV.

Furthermore, the geomagnetic field tends to modify the arrival directions so that detectors at a particular location do not preferentially detect particles arriving from their zenith direction. Thus although the arrival direction of particles can be deduced from the neutron intensities at various geographic locations, the task is not a simple one. It turns out that detectors in the polar regions receive particles from a wide range of very precisely defined trajectories beyond the geomagnetic field. Thus an analysis of the neutron intensity records from polar region detectors is most informative as to arrival directions.

For the May 4 event the increases in neutron intensity were widely different for the seven polar region detectors. A detector at Churchill, Canada, that accepts particles only from a narrow cone in the equatorial plane recorded an increase of 300 percent. A similar detector at College, Alaska, receiving particles from a quite different direction recorded about a 10 percent increase. A marked asymmetry in the particle arrival directions is indicated thereby.

These asymmetries suggest that the particles traveled along magnetic field lines that originated at the solar west limb and made an angle at the earth of about 55° with the earth-sun line. Particles that missed the earth did not return, as none were detected from the opposite direction. Thus it would appear that interplanetary fields like those shown in Fig. 4-10b are required to explain the asymmetries in arrival direction. However, it is not clear whether those fields were prepared in some bottle form by the preceding flares or whether they were left in that form after passage of a plasma blast wave.

A very troublesome point is illustrated by the particle transit times found for these high-energy events. In the May 4 case, the transit time was 22 minutes. Now the transit time for a 10^9 eV proton moving from the sun to the earth at low pitch angle along the spiral field lines shown in Fig. 4-10a is only about 12 minutes! Where the particles spent the other 10 minutes is not known, although it is sometimes supposed that they are stored in the vicinity of the sun for these periods. There is at this time no other evidence of such storage. Arguments have also been presented to suggest that the field lines, although grossly spiraled, are so tortuous as to account for the long transit times observed.

§ 4-4 **The Ionosphere.** Aside from lightning and the aurora, perhaps the longest-studied aspect of the plasma environment of the earth is the *ionosphere*. As early as 1902 the presence of an ionized layer in the upper atmosphere was postulated by Heaviside and Kennelly to account for the anomalously long distances radio waves could be propagated. Also at that time the ultraviolet radiation from the sun was suggested as providing the necessary ionization energy for production of the layer.

Present-day techniques for study of the ionosphere include the reflection and transmission of radio signals by the ionized material. The reflection technique, which has been used since 1925, involves the use of ground-based radio transmitters and receivers that measure the transit time required for signals transmitted from the earth to be reflected from various levels of the ionosphere. The reflection occurs from that region at which the local plasma frequency equals that of the electromagnetic signal. Of course, if the signal frequency exceeds the plasma frequency at every altitude, it is not reflected at all. By varying the frequency of the transmitted signal and measuring the signal transit time, the dependence of plasma frequency and hence, by Eq. 1-11, the electron density on

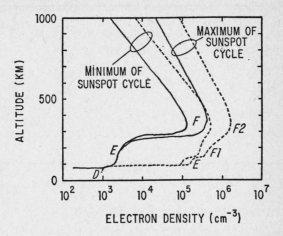

FIG. 4-11 Average electron densities as a function of altitude above the earth's surface for day (dashed curves) and night (solid curves), and solar maximum and minimum.

altitude can be deduced. Experiments to measure the transmission of the ionosphere are carried out by use of transmitter-equipped satellites.

Figure 4-11 shows plots of electron density as a function of altitude as determined by reflection techniques. Four different observational conditions are represented in these plots: daytime and nighttime, and solar cycle maximum and minimum. The very clear dependences upon the sun are obvious. Electron density is greater in the day than at night and greater at maximum than at minimum solar activity.

Beyond these gross changes there are also variations in the details of the electron density plots. In the daytime, a number of rather well-defined breaks in the curve occur. These breaks are even more sharply defined on a plot of transit time as a function of frequency because they are directly related to the plasma frequency at the level of each break. The breaks were at first interpreted as a series of ionospheric layers that were labeled D, E, F_1, F_2. However, the present evidence shown in Fig. 4-11 makes it clear that there are no actual layers within the ionosphere, but rather a more or less continual variation of ionization.

The time behavior of each of the ionization regions is interesting and somewhat complex. A few examples will be given. Associated with solar flares are sudden ionospheric disturbances. During these disturbances the D region ionization is markedly increased. In the polar regions the increased ionization may be so extensive as to prevent almost all radio noise from sources beyond the solar system from penetrating the ionosphere.

The day-to-night variation in the E region ionization is very great, amounting to something like two orders of magnitude in electron density. The E region is also subject to the short-term establishment of very thin layers of enhanced ionization at various levels. Observational studies of these so-called sporadic E layers continue, but no adequate explanation of their occurrence is available.

The F region is divided in daytime, but the division disappears at night. The variability of this region is much greater than the others.

To understand adequately these types of ionospheric behavior it is necessary to know not only how the solar radiation is absorbed and ionization produced, but also what the recombination rates are at various altitudes. Calculations of the absorption and recombinations have been made by using the known spectrum of the sun and the presently available data and theory of the atmospheric composition. The two electron density steps in the F region are thought to be due to the fact that, although the most effectively absorbed part of the solar spectrum from about 200 Å to 911 Å produces a maximum ionization at about the F_1 altitude, the recombination rate drops so rapidly with altitude that the maximum electron density occurs much higher. During the night the ionizing radiation is stopped, and the density of the F_1 region immediately drops as a result of recombination. However, the much lower recombination rate at higher altitudes holds up the electron density in the F_2 region throughout the night.

Solar radiation at wavelengths both above and below the 200 Å to 900 Å band penetrates the F region and produces the E region. Recombination rates are so large at this altitude that the E region is not expected to exist at night. It has been proposed that ionization by micrometeorites or meteorites might account for the observed nighttime E region, but it is not certain that this explanation is correct.

The D region is thought to be formed by the absorption of Lyman alpha (H_α) radiation at 1216 Å. This radiation can penetrate deeply into the ionosphere because of a gap in the molecular oxygen absorption spectrum that allows it to pass. The ionization in the D region seems to be due to trace amounts of nitric oxide, which has an ionization potential low enough for Lyman alpha to be effective. The D region disappears at night.

Ordinary long-wave radio broadcast reception is strongly influenced by ionospheric changes. Perhaps the most obvious effect is the difference between daytime and nighttime reception. Although very distant stations can be received at night, this is not possible during the day. The difference is due to the changing absorption in the ionosphere. During the day the high collision rates between electrons and neutral particles produce strong absorption of the electromagnetic waves. At night this collision rate is much reduced because of lower electron temperatures. Furthermore, at some level the electron density will have increased sufficiently that the plasma frequency equals that of the long-wavelength radio waves, which will then be reflected back to the ground.

§ 4-5 **Plasma Beyond the Solar System.**   Information about regions beyond the solar system is not easily obtained, since it is impossible to probe them with direct measuring instruments. Instead, reliance must be placed upon observation of the various radiations emitted by these regions. Because the distances are very great, the sensitivity requirements for detectors of this radiation are correspondingly severe.

Two types of radiation are received at the earth from regions beyond the solar system. Throughout the long history of astronomy, electromagnetic radiation, particularly in the visible wavelengths, has provided the bulk of observational information. During the past two decades, electromagnetic radiation at radio frequencies has supplied additional novel and important data unobtainable at visible wavelengths. Virtually everything now known about these distant regions rests upon the evidence of electromagnetic radiation in the close neighborhood of either 1.5×10^9/sec or 5×10^{14}/sec.

However, another source of information, perhaps not so thoroughly tapped, is also available. Cosmic rays, mostly protons with small admixtures of heavier nuclei, are generated and accelerated to high energy within and possibly between galaxies. Although little is now known about the production mechanisms of cosmic rays, ultimately it will certainly prove necessary to understand the role played by these high-energy particles in astrophysical systems.

In this section we discuss primarily the galactic structures that have become so evident since the studies of them were begun by Hubble. We describe certain of the optical and radio frequency evidence concerning these structures and how this evidence bears upon certain models of galaxies. Throughout this discussion it will be evident that much of the behavior of even these vast systems must depend in critical ways upon plasma and hydromagnetic behavior. Most of the details concerning plasma processes in these systems are lacking since the evidences are still so sparse and the inclusion of hydromagnetic phenomena into the models has occurred so recently. Nevertheless, it seems evident that more detailed observation and thought regarding these processes will yield substantial gains in understanding the galactic systems.

A casual examination of the photographs included in the National Geographic Society-Palomar Observatory Sky Survey or of plates taken with the 200-inch reflector at Palomar reveals two distinct types of astronomical objects. The individual stars that appear as points of light with unresolved detail are one. But far more prevalent are the extended, resolved sources that reveal structure. Closer study shows these objects to have a wide variety of forms. Whirls, swirls, and diffuse blobs of various shapes are seen. The vast majority of these objects are vast collections of stars and gas called *galaxies*.

From the earth the largest appearing of the galaxies is the Great Nebula in the constellation Andromeda. To the naked eye it appears as a small, hazy source of light. But in a photograph it has the form of a spiral viewed at about 15° from the spiral's plane. This spiral subtends about 3.5° of arc, or about seven times the apparent size of the moon! Thus much can be learned about this type of galaxy by study of this particularly well-resolved object. This galaxy, called M31, is 2×10^6 light years away and is the nearest of the large spiral galaxies. (A light year is the distance traveled by light in one year.)

Galaxies seem to be distributed throughout all space. Analysis of the light from galactic sources shows their spectral lines to be shifted toward the red wavelengths by variable amounts. This red shift, which is interpreted as a Doppler shift, implies that all galaxies are moving away from us at velocities that increase with increasing distance. Since our position is certainly not unique, all galaxies are expected to be receding from each other, thus participating in a universal expansion of galactic matter.

Furthermore, the more distant galaxies show the largest red shifts. In fact, the red shift appears to be directly proportional to the distance of the receding galaxy. Since the red shift is proportional to the recessional velocity, the velocity is proportional to the distance. The constant of this latter proportionality is called the Hubble constant after the astronomer who first recognized the relationship. The Hubble constant is approximately $H = 25$ km/sec per million light years, although because of uncertainties in the distance scale the value is subject to considerable controversy and to revision.

An implication of the galactic expansion is that at very great distances the spectral lines may become so far shifted to the red as to be undetectable. The Hubble constant gives a source velocity half that of light at distances of about 6×10^9 light years. A few objects, first identified by their radio emission, are of unknown structures and are currently called quasi-stellar sources. They have red shifts corresponding to such distances. Evidence from red shifts indicates that the density of galaxies is more or less uniform throughout the space from which light can be detected, although exact uniformity is not certain.

Another consequence of the observed expansion would seem to be that all the galactic matter should have been concentrated at the center of expansion at some remote time. The time at which this concentration is thought to have occurred is just the reciprocal of the Hubble constant, which, reduced to consistent units, is

$H = 25 \times 10^{19}$ cm/sec-cm. Thus the reciprocal of the Hubble constant is $H^{-1} \approx 10^{10}$ years. A possible conclusion of this line of reasoning is that an explosion of the then-concentrated matter of the universe occurred some 10^{10} years ago and that the presently observed expansion is the visible evidence of that ancient event.

The above is by no means the only interpretation of the expansion. Another proposal suggests the continuous creation and expansion of matter to form the steady state universe we observe today.

Galaxies have many different shapes and are generally classified accordingly. Since many of the other characteristics we later discuss will be shape dependent, we present the classification scheme. Figure 4-12 shows sketches of the various forms. Two general types

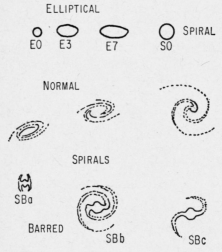

FIG. 4-12 Classification of the galaxies by their form.

occur, the elliptical and the disc-shaped. Elliptical galaxies are generally featureless and show a gradual drop in luminosity toward the edges. These galaxies are designated E followed by a number that increases with greater ellipticity. Disc-shaped galaxies may have spiral arms or may be almost featureless discs. The latter are labeled SO. Spirals may have a bar across the center (SB) or not (S). Increasingly open spirals are labeled Sa, Sb, Sc, respectively. M31 is classified Sb.

The striking shapes of the spirals have made them a favorite subject for observation and for conjecture. For example, the spiral arms suggest rotational motion, and the question of direction of rotation arises. The resolution of this question was not easy. Doppler measurements to yield rotational direction are easiest for galaxies viewed as nearly edge on as possible, but the arms are not discernible in this view. For galaxies tilted sufficiently to show structure, the Doppler shift becomes small. In spite of these difficulties, recent observations have shown that spirals do rotate in a direction such that the arms trail. Later we shall see the importance of this finding.

The sun is a star in an Sb (spiral) galaxy. The Milky Way is the visible evidence of this galaxy. Star counts within the Milky Way show the presence of the spiral arms. Were it not for obscuring dust clouds, the luminous, central nucleus of the galaxy would be visible from the earth. The central region, or nucleus, consists of clusters of stars that contain from thousands to millions of stars each. The central nucleus contains 10^8 to 10^9 solar masses within a diameter of about 30 light years (l.y.). The entire galaxy contains about 10^{11} stars and has a diameter of 100 000 l.y. The sun is located in one of the spiral arms, some 33 000 l.y. from the galactic center. The spiral arms are spaced at about 5000 l.y. The disc is about 2000 l.y. thick, and the sun is 30 l.y. from the midplane of the disc. The galaxy is also surrounded by a radio-frequency-emitting halo that is roughly spherical, with a diameter that may be as large as 200 000 l.y. This halo is not detectable in the visible wavelengths.

The rotational velocity of the part of the galaxy near the sun can be deduced from the Doppler shifts of neighboring galaxies. Among the motions contributing to these shifts is a common contribution, deduced to be 260 km/sec, which derives from rotation of our galaxy. This velocity yields one complete revolution of the galaxy at the sun's radial distance each 200×10^6 years. This amounts to 50 revolutions within the 10^{10} years given by the inverse of the Hubble constant. In view of this rapid rotation, the large number of spiral-armed structures presently observed constitutes an important question of galactic structure and stability because the rotation should quickly wind up the arms into a tight bundle. Therefore, either the arms are transitory structures that are frequently replaced, or else stabilizing forces must act to prevent their being wound up on themselves.

Another puzzle closely related to the stability and lifetime of the spiral arms is the presence of very luminous stars along them. The great luminosity and energy output of these stars denies them a long life, hence those observed now must be quite young. In addition to stars the arms also contain dust clouds and hydrogen gas from which the bright, young stars are actually observed to form. However, the supply of this material in our region of the galaxy is quite limited. At the present rate of star formation this material would last less than 10^9 years. The presence of these short-lived stars implies either the relative youth of the arms themselves or the action of some mechanism whereby material can be continuously supplied to the arms for star formation.

At the outset it must be said that neither of these puzzles has been solved. However, some additional evidence is available. It will first be presented; then some proposed galactic models will be discussed.

Light from stars in neighboring spiral arms is observed to be polarized. There is general agreement about the cause. Intervening dust clouds partially obscure the light from these stars. Elongated dust grains in these clouds, aligned by galactic magnetic fields, are thought to absorb preferentially the star light polarized along the major axis of the dust grains. Thus the light polarized perpendicular to the major axis is passed in larger amounts by the dust clouds. The magnetic fields thus observed near spiral arms are directed along those arms and are about 2×10^{-5} gauss.

Another, possibly related, observation is the outflow of material from the center of galaxies. This flow was first observed in our galaxy by measuring the Doppler shift of the 21-cm neutral hydrogen line. This line is in the radio frequency range (1420 megacycles) and is detected by means of radio telescopes. Flow speeds as high as 200 km/sec are observed near the galactic center and may be as high as 20 km/sec near the sun. Similar flow has been observed in M31 by optical means with the 200-inch Palomar reflector. The rate at which matter streams from the central region is about one solar mass per year. According to this estimate the central region would be emptied in 10^8 to 10^9 years if it were unreplenished.

The observation of a flow of material and of a magnetic field along the spiral arms tempts the use of a hydromagnetic model. Even though the flow is observed to be mostly neutral hydrogen, sufficient ion densities should be present to keep the ion-neutral collision distances small compared to the dimensions of the system. Further, the Debye distance from Eq. 1-1 is $D = 6.90(T/n_e)^{1/2}$ cm, where T is in degrees Kelvin and n_e in cm^{-3}. Thus even for T as high as 10^6 °K and n_e as low as 10^{-14} cm^{-3}, D is under one light year. Nevertheless, considerable caution is necessary in treating such a complex system on such evidence. Any proposed model must be considered as highly speculative.

At one time it was thought that the various galactic forms shown in Fig. 4-12 represented an evolutionary development. Galaxies were thought to exist first as compact rotating EO galaxies. The angular momentum was supposed to cause the galaxy to flatten into progressively elliptical forms until the disc-like SO stage was reached. Further rotation was then imagined to fling out the galactic arms, which slowly dissipated into intergalactic space, leaving the highly irregular systems such as the nearby Magellanic Clouds.

Recent determinations of galactic masses throw serious doubt upon an evolutionary scheme of this sort. The masses can be deduced from the many pairs of galaxies that are observed in the Palomar Sky Survey photographs. Assuming that the pairs are in gravitationally bound orbits about each other, it is possible to calculate their masses. Such mass determinations indicate the spheroidal and elliptical galaxies to be about 30 times as massive as the spirals. It is difficult to see how these more massive galaxies could dispense so large a fraction of their mass to evolve into spirals. Thus it is generally believed that the galactic forms represent entirely different type galaxies that have little, if any, evolutionary connection.

We return to the specific discussion of spiral galaxies and consider two forms of a highly speculative hydromagnetic model for such objects. We first consider the galaxy as a steady state system in which whatever dynamic processes are acting can continue for times of the order of 10^{10} years. Suppose the galaxy has an over-all magnetic dipole field oriented as shown in Fig. 4-13a. This field might have been generated by the flow of plasma currents in a self-exciting dynamo action, such as is believed to provide the

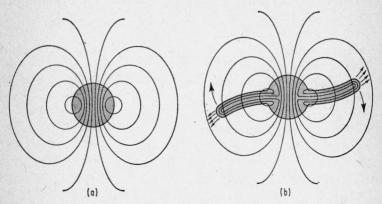

FIG. 4-13 (a) An assumed magnetic dipole field for a spiral galaxy. (b) Perturbed dipole field due to the flow of slightly ionized material along the galactic arms.

terrestrial dipole field. Possibly the radial outflow from the central nucleus could be one part of the required current system. This outflow may be driven in part by the rotational forces of the galaxy. If the outflow were confined to a few azimuthal regions, the armed structure could be formed. The observed one solar mass per year could easily supply the material necessary for new-star formation. Moreover, the slightly ionized material would draw out the magnetic field lines along the spiral arms, as is observed. The resulting galactic magnetic field would then appear as in Fig. 4-13b.

As the spiral arms extended outward farther and farther from the central region, the flow speeds would decrease. However, the field lines that are shown closed in Fig. 4-13b may not be able to prevent the slow diffusion of material out into the general dipole field. That field, in turn, may funnel an appreciable fraction back into the central region. There the material would partake of the more violent activity of that region until it is once again ejected along a spiral arm.

Such a model has several attractive features. It correlates the observed radial flow with the observed magnetic fields along the arms. It provides material for new-star formation in the arms. It provides a radial motion that, coupled with the rotation, would tend to keep the arms from becoming wound upon themselves. But the model also has problems. It is doubtful that the measured outflow is at all adequate to keep the arms open. There is little evidence for the over-all dipole field we have supposed. There is no evidence for recirculation.

An alternate to such a steady state model is suggested by dropping the requirement that the spiral arms are fixed features. If they are transitory, some mechanism must be provided whereby they can be generated frequently during the life of the galaxy. At least two possibilities have been suggested. One is that the central regions of certain galaxies undergo frequent and violent explosions that result in the ejection from those regions of vast quantities of matter and energy. Although few details of this suggestion have been worked out, such an explosion is thought to have occurred in the galaxy M82.

One possible means whereby the explosion could occur might be the triggering of an extensive series of bursts in a region of high stellar density by a supernova explosion. A supernova explosion is probably caused by the sudden collapse of a star which results from an excess of gravitational pressure over radiation pressure. The gravitational collapse is highly regenerative because of a combination of gravitational and nuclear effects, and a sizable fraction of the total gravitational energy can be released within a period of seconds. Supernova explosions are observed to occur in galaxies within our easy view at the rate of several per year. If a large central region could be triggered by such a burst, the galactic center might act as a kind of super supernova. In order to account entirely for the observed galactic features, such as spiral arms of short lifetime and intense radio frequency emission, galactic centers would have to explode many times during a galactic lifetime.

A second suggestion is that the central region is immersed at the center of a dipole field like that shown in Fig. 4-13a and that flute-like instabilities of the type discussed in § 2-2 develop. These instabilities might then drive plasma material out across field lines and produce disturbances like those shown in Fig. 4-13b. The ejected material and fields would constitute the spiral arms and presumably could dissipate with a lifetime much less than that of the galaxy. The present abundance of spiral-armed galaxies might, however, be maintained by the recurrent development of new instabilities.

Electromagnetic radiation at radio frequencies can be detected at the earth from a variety of astronomical objects. Such emissions come from the sun, certain planets, nearby stars, and galaxies. The wavelength of this radiation ranges from a few centimeters to several meters and can be classified into three types. From regions of high temperature (for example, near hot stars) comes a continuous spectrum of emission. The intensity of this spectrum decreases with increasing wavelength like the radiation from a black body. It thus derives from thermal processes the most likely of which is bremsstrahlung from electron collisions with interstellar nuclei.

From regions of relatively low temperature where the gas is mostly neutral, radiation at 21-cm wavelength is observed. This radiation is emitted by hydrogen atoms when the electron and nuclear spins change from a parallel to an antiparallel state.

By far the largest amount of radio emission is nonthermal (that is, the intensity increases with wavelength) and comes from localized sources such as galaxies and other nebulous regions.

It has been possible to make extensive surveys of the sky at radio wavelengths, and a large number of localized sources of radiation have been detected. Furthermore, the positions of more than a hundred of these sources have been determined with sufficient accuracy to allow identification of the corresponding optical objects. In almost every case the source has turned out to be a galaxy, usually elliptical. The special case of a supernova is discussed presently.

The identification of the radio sources with galaxies is most fortunate, since Doppler shifts can be measured for the optical objects and their distances thereby fixed. With the distance known, the rate of energy emission can be calculated.

Perhaps the most striking thing about these localized radio sources is their enormous radio frequency energy output, which commonly substantially exceeds that radiated in the visible by a typical galaxy. Radio emission rates of 10^{44} ergs/sec are observed. If this rate were to persist for 10^9 years $\approx 3 \times 10^{16}$ sec, a total radio energy of 3×10^{60} ergs would be emitted. Now a typical energy equivalent to the entire mass of a galaxy is only 10^{66} ergs. Therefore, in accounting for such vast emissions, processes capable of transferring a galactic mass into radiation with efficiencies approaching 10^{-5} must be imagined.

Another dominant characteristic of the localized radio sources is their nonthermal frequency dependence, mentioned earlier. This dependence implies that radiation and small-scale turbulences do not constitute the principal energy exchange mechanisms that produce the emitted energy.

A conceivable process whereby the large amounts of nonthermal radiation might be generated is the central region explosions referred to above. However, the details of how the subsequent transformation to radio energy might take place is not yet evident.

A possible process, which is observed to operate in some cases, occurs in the Crab nebula. The Crab nebula is the remnant of a supernova explosion that was recorded by Oriental astronomers in 1054 A.D. The Crab is a strong radio source, is located in our galaxy, and is easily observed using optical and radio telescopes.

An important characteristic of the radiation from this source is that it is strongly linearly polarized. In fact, with optical and 3-cm-wavelength radio telescopes and polarization analysis, radiation from various portions of the object are seen to possess different polarizations, but definite patterns are apparent in the polarization. Figure 4-14 is a sketch of the Crab showing the direction and magnitude of polarization of the light coming from the various regions.

It is well known from electromagnetic theory and from laboratory experiments that electrons traveling at close to the speed of light in a magnetic field can radiate copious amounts of energy. This radiating property is a consequence of the circular motion executed by the electrons in the magnetic field. The field exerts a radial force upon the electrons, thereby inducing the circular motion. The consequent radial acceleration of the electrons causes them to radiate energy. This radiation is called *synchrotron radiation*, since

50% POLARIZATION

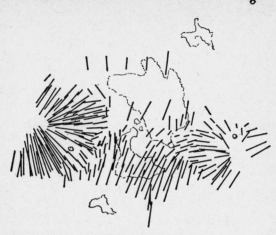

FIG. 4-14 Sketch of the Crab nebula showing the directions of polarization of the emitted radiation. The lightly sketched lines crudely represent the optical object. The solid lines show the direction and percentage of polarization observed. (From Hiltner, *Astrophysical Journal*, Vol. 125, p. 300, 1957)

it was first identified as the light emitted by electrons in circular orbits in a particle accelerator called the synchrotron.

That accelerated electrons will radiate energy is easily surmised by noting that radio waves are generated by oscillating (hence accelerated) electrons in a radio transmitting antenna. In a transmitting antenna the waves are polarized so that the electric field vector is parallel to the oscillatory electron motion. The same polarization occurs in the radiation from circling electrons in a magnetic field, and the plane of polarization is perpendicular to the direction of the field.

On this basis it is believed that the polarized light emitted by the Crab nebula comes from high-energy electrons moving in the local magnetic fields that are directed perpendicular to the observed polarization direction of the light.

Since the Crab is the remnant of a supernova in which large amounts of ionization energy were available, the complex magnetic field pattern was probably formed by the twisting and distortion of the original field distribution as it was dragged about by the highly conducting, turbulent plasma motions produced by the explosion. Thus we see that in an object of this sort the combined effects of plasma motion and magnetic fields have played a most significant part.

From energy considerations it is believed that the high-energy electrons required to produce the synchrotron radiation are the decay products of the so-called pi mesons that could certainly have been produced by nuclear collisions induced by the supernova explosion.

Extending these ideas from supernova to galaxies, it is now commonly supposed that synchrotron radiation accounts for the radiation from a large fraction of the nonthermal, galactic radio sources. The polarization that must characterize such sources has been detected optically in the case of the galaxy M87. This elliptical galaxy has what appears to be a jet of material extending to one side, and the light from this jet is strongly polarized. Polarizations from a number of radio sources have been observed, and this evidence strongly supports the synchrotron radiation mechanism.

On a galactic scale, the energy required for pi meson production may come from explosions in central regions, perhaps triggered by supernova as described above, or conceivably from gravitational energy released during formation.

The shape of many of the radio emission regions about the optical galaxies seems to suggest an explosion mechanism. Figure 4-15 shows the optical and radio emission regions of the source Cygnus A superimposed. The optical galaxy occupies only a small volume compared to the radio regions, which are displaced symmetrically about it at very great distances. The occurrence of such double regions of emission from radio sources is very common.

For radio sources with identifiable visible components, the Doppler shifts of lines from the visible components and the Hubble constant yield the distances to the sources. With the distances known, the volume of the radio emitting region can be estimated from the apparent size of the source. Given the volume, the measured emitted power, and the assumption of the synchrotron radiating mechanism, a value of the required magnetic fields can be

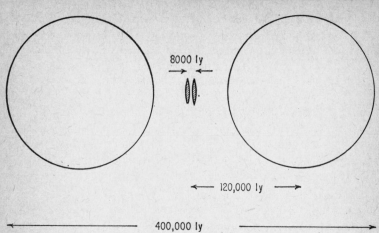

8000 ly

120,000 ly

400,000 ly

FIG. 4-15 Superposition of the optical and radio emission regions of
the Cygnus A system.

deduced. For most radio sources the fields so calculated turn out
to be of the order of 10^{-5} gauss, a value close to that observed in
our own galaxy.

In spite of a great deal of observational evidence, suggestions
about galactic evolution and stability remain essentially speculative. Much more evidence and analysis is required before suitable
explanations of these vast systems will be possible.

Bibliography

L. Spitzer, *Physics of Fully Ionized Gases* (Interscience Publishers, Inc., New York, 1962), 2nd Ed.

T. G. Cowling, *Magnetohydrodynamics* (Interscience Publishers, Inc., New York, 1957).

H. Alfvén, *Cosmical Electrodynamics* (Oxford University Press, 1953).

J. W. Dungey, *Cosmic Electrodynamics* (Cambridge University Press, 1958).

F. M. Penning, *Electrical Discharges in Gases* (Macmillan Co., New York, 1957).

A. S. Bishop, *Project Sherwood* (Addison-Wesley Publishing Company, Reading, Mass., 1958).

D. J. Rose and M. Clark, *Plasma and Controlled Fusion* (John Wiley, New York, 1961).

J. J. Thomson, *Conduction of Electricity Through Gases* (Cambridge University Press, 1906).

F. Clauser, *Plasma Dynamics* (Addison-Wesley Publishing Co., Reading, Mass., 1960).

F. S. Johnson, *Satellite Environment Handbook* (Stanford University Press, 1961).

H. C. van de Hulst, C. de Jager, A. F. Moore, editors, *Space Research, Proceedings of the Second International Space Science Symposium, 1961* (North-Holland Publishing Co., Amsterdam, 1961).

Index